Brave New World?

LIVING WITH INFORMATION TECHNOLOGY

Macdonald & Co
LONDON & SYDNEY

This paperback edition first published in Great
Britain in 1982 by
Macdonald & Co (Publishers) Ltd
London & Sydney

Maxwell House
74 Worship Street
London EC2A 2EN

Front cover design by Theo Hodges
Co-ordinated by Rhona Gibbs, Namemakers Ltd.

ISBN 0 356 09178 3

Printed in Great Britain by A. Wheaton & Co. Ltd. Exeter

Contents

Preface

Message by Kenneth Baker MP, Minister of State for Industry and Information Technology, for Brave New World?

The microelectronics revolution that we have been talking about for the past few years has spawned an even bigger revolution — Information Technology.

By providing components that are even smaller, cheaper and more reliable, microelectronics has transformed computers and telecommunications. The changes in individual devices have been staggering, but the totality of IT is greater than the sum of its parts. The widespread use and linking of computer systems is creating a society where information itself is our most precious raw material.

It is vital that everyone in this country — school children, the general public, industry, trade and commerce — should recognise the importance of IT, and should exploit it to their own advantage. It is not an esoteric technology, but we have to make a conscious effort to come to terms with it. This publication will play a valuable role in improving our understanding and extending the application of IT skills.

Reader's Chapter Briefings

B NW – A*

Glossary of Terms

Analogue. A continuous relationship between information and its representation, any part of which merges imperceptibly into the next, eg, a sound wave is an analogue representation of the sound.

APL. *A Programming Language.* A program language which needs little or no previous computing knowledge.

ATM. *Automated Teller Machine*, eg. NatWest's Servicetill.

BACS. *Bankers Automated Clearing Service* – established in 1967 by the major banks.

Bar-coded label. A label which holds data coded in the form of lines of various thickness. Commonly used in supermarkets.

Baseband. A low capacity telecommunications link; carrying mainly data.

BASIC. *Beginners All-purpose Symbolic Instruction Code.* A programming language which is very simple to learn and useful for educational purposes, commonly used with microcomputers.

Bit. Abbreviation for *BInary digiT* (value of 0 or 1).

Broadband. (or wideband): a high-capacity telecommunications link. Capable of carrying voice and video.

Bubble memory. A new compact form of magnetic technology for mass storage of data, which may gain acceptance as an alternative to tape and disc memories. Non-volatile and therefore it retains its data even when power has been switched off.

Bus network. A type of LAN enabling the different parts of an electronic system to communicate with each other.

Byte. 8 bits. This is a unit of information commonly used to represent a character.

CAD/CAM. Computer *A*ided *D*esign/*C*omputer *A*ided *M*anufacture.

CEEFAX. The BBC's teletext service.

Central Processing Unit (CPU). Traditionally the main hardware control unit of a computer, comprising: processor, main memory and input/output controller.

CHAPS. *C*learing *H*ouse *A*utomated *P*ayments *S*ystem.

CHIPS. *C*learing *H*ouse *I*nter-bank *P*ayments *S*ystem.

CNC. *C*omputerised *N*umerical *C*ontrol.

Co-axial cable. Cable with one wire running within and insulated from another – like TV aerial cabling in the home.

COBOL. *CO*mmon *B*usiness *O*rientated *L*anguage. The most commonly used commercial programming language.

COM. *C*omputer *O*utput *M*icrofilm.

CP/M. *C*ontrol *P*rogram (for) *M*icrocomputers. A commonly used program which organises the internal operation of the computer.

Cursor. An indicator on a VDU screen showing the next position for entering data onto the screen.

Database. A pool of shared information held on computer storage. It allows several users to access the same information, obviating the need to maintain their own personal files.

DBS. *D*irect *B*roadcasting *S*atellite transmissions.

Digital. When information is represented as a sequence of numbers that change in finite steps, the numbered sequence is referred to as digital data.

Direct access. Stored information that can be accessed directly from memory regardless of its location, e.g. discs. *See also* **Serial access.**

DP. *D*ata *P*rocessing.

EDP. *E*lectronic *D*ata *P*rocessing.

EFT. *E*lectronic *F*unds *T*ransfer – moving money and financial instruments by computer-to-computer communications.

Electronic mail. The transmission of information and correspondence by electronic means instead of by the ordinary postal service. Telex is an example familiar to most people.

EPOS. *E*lectronic *P*oint *O*f *S*ale terminal.

Floppy disc. A flexible disc used for storing information. Similar in appearance to a 45 rpm record. A direct access method of retrieving information.

FORTRAN. *FOR*mula *TRAN*slation. The most widely used scientifically orientated language.

Gateway. A link and a method of passing information between one network and another – typically in the form of an interface device and/or a common protocol.

Hardcopy. The physical output which can physically be taken away and read when desired, e.g. printout on paper, microfilm, microfiche, etc.

Hardware. The physical part of a computing system – the equipment, and components, e.g. terminals, discs, memory, etc.

Input. The data transferred into the computer.

K. Symbol for 1,000 or 1,024 depending on usage. In computer-related matters, although it stands for 1,024 it is taken to mean 1,000. So 4Kb theoretically = 4,096 bits: but it is loosely interpreted as 4,000 bits.

Kb. *Ki*lo*b*its (thousands of bits).

KB. *Ki*lo*b*ytes.

LAN. *L*ocal *A*rea *N*etwork.

Lightpen. A pen-like device using a ray of light and photocells to read particular forms of data, e.g. bar codes.

Magnetic tape. A method of storing data on a plastic tape treated with a magnetisable oxide material. Similar to tape used on a domestic tape recorder. Information retrieval by serial access.

Mainframe. Adjective generally used to describe large computers.

Memory. This term can refer to all forms of computer storage, but is generally used in connection with the main memory. A device which can retain information for retrieval at a later date.

Microcomputer. A very small computer that uses a microprocessor for its Central Processing Unit (CPU).

Microfiche. Rectangular sheets of photographic film holding reduced micro-images of text.

Microfilm. Reduction of text into micro-images held on a film strip, rather than on a flat sheet as described above.

Microprocessor. A single microelectronic chip containing all the electronic logic of a Central Processing Unit (CPU).

Minicomputer. A misleading term – very similar in size and function to a mainframe.

Off-line. Operations related to computer tasks which are not carried out directly connected to a computer. The opposite to on-line.

Optical Character Recognition (OCR). Characters that are recognised and read automatically by a machine.

ORACLE. The IBA's teletext service.

Output. Information or results produced by a computer into either hardcopy or softcopy formats.

PABX. *P*rivate *A*utomatic *B*ranch *E*xchange.

Packet switching. A method of transmitting blocks of data, with an allocated address, via a network, to its destination.

PIN. *P*ersonal *I*dentification *N*umber.

PLC. *P*rogrammable *L*ogic *C*ontroller – similar to a minicomputer in operation, but it is not reprogrammable.

Prestel. The trademark used by British Telecom for their viewdata system – giving general and business information.

Printout. *See* **Hardcopy.**

Program. A sequence of instructions which inform the central processing unit how to carry out the necessary operations to fulfil the user's requirements.

PROM. *P*rogrammable *R*ead-*O*nly *M*emory. A type of 'read-only' memory which can be programmed by the user.

Ring network. A LAN whose cable goes round in a joined loop, with individual terminals connected to the loop.

Sequential access. *See* **Serial access.**

Serial access. Stored information that is extracted by searching sequentially through the storage medium.

Softcopy. Information read on a VDU screen.

Software. The programs read into and stored by the computer's main memory. The hardware then utilises the program to fulfil the user's requirements.

Solid State. Refers to the branch of physics that concerns itself with the essential properties of semiconductor materials. The term can therefore be used more or less as a synonym for semiconductors.

Star network. Star LANs are based on the PABX and have a number of cables radiating out from the central exchange.

SWIFT. *S*ociety for *W*orldwide *I*nterbank *F*inancial *T*elecommunication.

System X. British Telecom's new all-electronic digital telephone exchanges.

Telemetry. The reading of meters from a distance – possibly using the existing telecommunications network.

Teletext. A generic term for information, textually displayed on a television screen which is broadcast through a television company, e.g. CEEFAX (BBC) and ORACLE (IBA).

Timesharing. An on-line system which several users can access simultaneously via their terminals.

User-friendly. User/machine compatability – a system which appeals to people who have little or no computer experience.

Videotex. An internationally accepted term for viewdata and teletext.

Viewdata. A generic term for information textually displayed on a television screen which is transmitted via telephone lines, e.g. Prestel.

Visual Display Unit (VDU). A television-like display screen with an accompanying keyboard.

VLSI. *V*ery *L*arge *S*cale *I*ntegration. Densely packed chips with high-performance capabilities within a very small space.

Word processor. A system which basically processes forms of text.

Part One

1

Brave New World?

PETER LARGE

Technology Correspondent of The Guardian

INFORMATION is wealth, and wide and swift access to information is power. That is the credo of information technology. It is a truism ages old, understood long before Francis Bacon defined it in 1597. Charles II grasped it, less than 70 years later, when he put information technology to work through the infant Post Office — so that he could read his enemies' letters and thus forestall the sort of conspiracy that cost his father his head.

The key to that power today lies in an object little bigger than a shirt button and slim enough to slip through the eye of a needle. It is, of course, the silicon chip — man's first universal machine, a machine now so microscopically intricate that the latest designs put the equivalent of a street map of greater London, back alleys and all, onto each of these tiny slivers of silicon.

Microchips are the engines of information technology. By making computers cheaper, smaller and more versatile, they have made it economic to bring wider automation to the office — and total automation to the factory. Therefore, within the next 20 years, information technology could affect working lives more profoundly than did the nineteenth century shift from the land to the cities.

So how do we define information technology in today's more complicated context? Judging by the number of descriptions around, it parallels the hoary joke about defining an elephant: at least you know it when you see it. There are said to be at least 30 definitions so far, most

3

of them using the neater French term *l'informatique* (informatics). The Académie Française produced one of the first definitions of informatics in 1967:

> "The science of the rational handling of information, particularly through computers and particularly in support of knowledge and communications in the technical, economic and social fields."

The definition of information technology favoured by the British Cabinet's technological advisory council is borrowed from Unesco:

> "Scientific, technological and engineering disciplines and the management techniques used in information handling and processing; their applications; computers and their interaction with men and machines; and associated social, economic and cultural matters."

Therefore, the clumsier British phrase, information technology, at least has the advantage of avoiding the need for another bit of jargon —telematics (French again, *la télématique*). Telematics covers the nitty-gritty of informatics — the skills and machines involved in the new information industries born of the convergence of telecommunications and computing, a range that spreads down from communications satellites and cable networks, through office computers and factory robots, to 'intelligent' typewriters and the domestic television set.

The academic theory behind information technology is plain sailing. Professor Tom Stonier, of Bradford University, one of the new breed of multi-disciplinary academics, has presented it in a structure of three industrial revolutions.

The first dealt with machines that extended human muscles; the second with machines that extended the human nervous system (radio, television, telephones, films); and the third, the computer-based information revolution, producing a post-industrial economy, deals with machines that extend the human brain. At all these stages the codified human skills required for the creation of wealth have intensified. In the final stage information itself becomes the key economic resource, demoting the traditional factors of production, such as capital and labour, and reducing manufacture of goods to an automated backwater.

Most of that is orthodoxy. The only major point of debate — apart from varying judgments of the time-scale of change — is whether new jobs, in the economic sense in which we now understand jobs, will still emerge to replace the old, as they did with the slower, less ubiquitous technological changes of the past.

But enough of theory. The time is overdue to illustrate practically that information is indeed wealth, and there is a sound example in that most down-to-earth of places, the sewer.

The sewers and water mains of most English cities were built in Victorian times. For more than a century those sub-cities of pipes have muddled along. Millions of nasty man hours and many millions of pounds have been wasted simply because no-one has known what goes on down there. Now, thanks to the microchip, area water authorities are finding out — cheaply.

In the West of England, the Wessex Water Authority spent about £50,000 in the late 1970s on surveying water flows and pressures across the region. Then, area by area, it began to use that new knowledge to introduce computer controls. By the autumn of 1979 the authority was estimating that savings would soon be running at £150,000 to £200,000 a year. In fact, by 1982 savings are around £1,000,000 a year, and the process of automation is still by no means complete. It has to be conceded, though, that some of those economies come from using the computer to postpone capital expenditure on renewing ageing sewers and water mains. The savings have been achieved in four main ways:

1. Electricity consumption is cut by adjusting water pressures to real needs. One of the best examples is at Swanage, in Dorset, where the night pressure has been reduced by half, saving more than £3000 a year in that small town alone.
2. Water wastage is cut by a huge reduction in the number of bursts in mains.
3. Staffing costs are cut, mainly by the consequent reduction in emergency overtime work.
4. Capital expenditure is cut by more precise knowledge of the needs. The biggest example here is the scrapping — or, at least, the postponement for a long time — of a plan to build an £800,000

reservoir. The survey illuminated a better option: to supply that particular increase in demand from elsewhere in the region, at a cost of £100,000.

The computer network that has achieved all that uses electronic instruments, spread over five counties, measuring and controlling the flows along the pipes as well as at source in rivers and reservoirs. Yet it depends essentially on one cheap microcomputer at the Wessex authority's headquarters in Bristol.

Around the microcomputer has been built a database of all useful information about the water supply and sewage systems in the region. The database includes 4000 maps, pinpointing every pipe and hydrant; a system to interpret faults reported by the recording instruments — with predictions of their impact; a directory of towns and villages, with details of the people to be contacted in emergencies; the current state of water storage in the reservoirs and the historical pattern of fluctuations of supply and (holiday area) demand throughout the year; the same sort of information about the weather; and a directory of chemicals, illustrating what needs to be done, if, say, a crashed road tanker's load gets into the sewers.

The system can therefore be used both for planning work and emergency decisions. It will spill its information in statistical, map, or multi-coloured graph form on the display screens; and it has been designed for use by people unaccustomed to computers — advice appears on the screens to guide the user into the next stage of his search for decision-forming information. The equipment cost less than £40,000 and the microcomputer itself was, inevitably, the cheapest item. Most of the money went on data storage discs and on the digital plotter that converts maps into computer data.

The regional controller (one man monitors the whole five-counties region through the night) can in emergency rally his information in seconds. Previously, he had to dig into card-index cabinets and check duty rosters. Now not only does that information appear on his computer screen in a co-ordinated bundle; he also has the statistics and the calculating power to adjust water pressures precisely and quickly if a main bursts.

The broad principle of the computer network is the same wherever it goes. The chips down the sewers (or, for that matter, down a coal mine or spread around the automated factory) are doing the same job as the airline booking networks which have been working for years, handling seat reservations for 250 airlines world-wide; or the financial networks that link over 500 banks in nearly 20 countries; or an individual company's database, dealing with personal records or financial analyses and disgorging its information onto computer terminals thousands of miles from head office; or a police computer from which an officer on the beat can in seconds extract details of a suspect via his radio; or a computer-run supermarket checkout which tells a central computer what you and thousands of others buy, so that stocks can be replenished quickly.

The most spectacular networks are those which use the logic of computerised telecommunications to dent our human conceptions of space and time. For instance, if one makes a purchase by American Express card in some Paris stores, the transaction involves a journey of about 46,000 miles completed in under seven seconds.

The computerised till in the store reads the information imbedded magnetically in the card and passes that information to the store's computers... which send the message by phone line to American Express's regional computers in Brighton... which send the message via line and space satellite to American Express's computer centre in Phoenix, Arizona... which checks that the card is not stolen and that one's credit is good for that amount of money... and back comes the answer, again bounced off the satellite, 22,500 miles up... and thus, within five to seven seconds of one's card first being placed in the till, the cashier at the counter knows the verdict.

Here is an even odder example. The fire brigade at Malmo, in Sweden, relies on a map which indicates the contents and fire risks of each factory in the area. When fire breaks out, smoke detectors not only alert the fire brigade, but also trigger a transatlantic message to computers in Cleveland, Ohio, which hold that electronic map. Before the firemen have had time to leave the station, a computer terminal in the fire engine is already displaying the advice bounced back from the Cleveland computers.

That particular use of distant computers is called time-sharing, because hundreds of organisations can thereby use a battery of big computers all at the same time. Small organisations such as the Malmo fire brigade have often found it cheaper and faster to hire computer power in this fashion. However, the advance of the cheap micro-computer is changing that. Today, for a few hundred pounds, one can buy a little box containing computer power that would have cost £10,000,000 and required roomfuls of machinery less than 30 years ago. Therefore, many organisations that in the past have used time-sharing services or their local equivalent, the computer bureau, are joining first-time computer users in doing the job themselves.

Therefore, too, the time-sharing services are turning increasingly to another type of international network: the specialised information bank. It is possible to get instant access to nearly 25,000,000 abstracts of scientific, technical and professional papers from such banks, and their number and size are growing. That is just one example of the further acceleration of change that the microchip, in its adolescence, is bringing to an industry which throughout its 30-year life has thrived on change. It is easy to forget what the old-fashioned computer industry has already achieved. In less than 20 years the industrialised world has come to rely on the computer: without it, government, commerce and defence could no longer function. Our society would collapse.

Then the second-phase expansion of the chip's capabilities in the mid-70s begat the cheap desk-top microcomputer and, equally signifi-cantly, hastened the convergence of the telecommunications and computer businesses, destroying their relatively cosy boundaries. Now everybody is jostling everybody else in the race to supply the tools of the electronic office. Computer companies are racing into communica-tions; telecommunications companies are sharpening their computer expertise; both sectors are increasingly making their own microchips, rather than relying totally on the chip industry; the chip industry is increasingly spreading beyond the chips themselves into office systems; while, most frantically of all, those companies that make more mundane office equipment, such as duplicators, are reshaping in order to offer the total office-automation package as well.

That upheaval presages a parallel new world for those companies' customers. Already industrial products accustomed to a decade or more of life are being cut off in their prime as a new breed of chip reshapes them or resharpens their production processes. Meanwhile, the next stage of the overall process is beginning. That is the extension of information technology to the home.

Before 1990, if present plans mature, most town-dwellers will be able to have a score or more international, national and local television channels piped into their homes; and, riding on the back of that multi-channel cable and satellite television, could come a hundred or more computer services — for those who can afford them. These services, already starting to appear, could play havoc with many traditional trades and professions, again destroying neat business —and trade union — boundaries. Here are just a few examples:

Income tax

The average innumerate citizen never thinks of employing a tax consultant. He or she struggles with the annual form with irritable inefficiency. A two-way computer service, like British Telecom's Prestel, which enables its users to cross-question central computers via the television screen, could offer question and answer sessions which would virtually complete that form for the average employee or self-employed businessman — and make sure that they did not miss any allowances.

Holidays and travel

One would no longer need to go to a travel agent or wait eternally on the phone for rail or airline inquiry offices to condescend to answer. One could book trains, flights, hotel rooms, excursions (and pay for them electronically by credit-card code) from the home television. One might also base those holiday decisions on video tours sent down the cable.

Home-hunting

One could tell the computer to put on the screen details (pictures as well as words) of all the houses available not more than 10 miles but not less than five from, say, Bristol city centre, costing between £40,000 and £65,000 and with gardens front and back. The list sent down the cable could be culled from a half a dozen estate agents.

Newspapers

No longer need they be centrally printed, carted round the country, and finally delivered to homes when their news and analysis can be five to ten hours out of date. Experiments with home print-outs of newspapers, providing an electronic facsimile of the printed page, began in Tokyo in 1978.

Politics

Democracy could — if we want — become literally government by the people, and instant government at that, with daily push button voting, even on secondary issues. In some US cities, where cable television links most of the homes, electronic polling has been used to test voters' views on local government issues. In 1978 the British Government's think tank, the Central Policy Review Staff, warned the Cabinet:

> "Any interactive television system, such as Prestel, provides a potential channel for a poll which is immediate, cheap and increasingly universal... The potential influence on the processes of both central and local government is substantial."

These examples only skim the least tender parts of the surface. When the distilled experience and knowledge of leading specialists become available in a computer's memory, poised for a dialogue, what happens to the routine lawyer and the average don? But all that is futurology, albeit of the near future. There are more urgent problems about the acceleration of change that information technology is causing and these are technical as well as social.

The computer has been around for more than 30 years now and the microprocessor for a dozen, yet we still have not mastered the complexities of our own creation. Economics is a tempting if inexact analogy, in that we have evolved systems that go beyond our ability to manage them.

The problems begin with the hardware, the machinery itself, but really blossom when we get to the software, the written instructions that tell the hardware what to do. On the hardware side, today's microprocessors, containing many thousands of microscopic components, have to be taken to some extent on trust: it has become impossible, even by computer, to test them sufficiently to ensure that they do indeed perform all the thousands of functions for which they are designed.

Those problems multiply when hundreds of microchips are put to work in a computer proper. Many design teams spend fewer months in producing the design of a new computer than they do in 'debugging' it, actually making it work. It's a bit like creating a multi-dimensional crossword puzzle which then has to be solved. One British computer designer uses the analogy of the steam engine: successive generations built by rule of thumb till we found the rules of thermodynamics. He calls it the Victorian bedstead syndrome: you fix one spring and another pops up, you know not why or how. It is not so much the awesome basics, millions of bits of information shunting about in pulsing sequences measured in billionths of a second: the design logic of all that can be tested by computer simulation. It is what can go wrong operationally in that shifting microscopic jungle, and the new effects when mere humans try to change it.

The problems include the microchips themselves; not just the failures but those that do not work at quite the regulation speed. Then there is the gathering of the chips into teams of circuit boards, with thousands of inter-connections. Then there is the relationship of the boards to each other and to the computer's outside sources of help, like storage discs. One fault in those multiple sequences can send the computer into the wasteland, endlessly circling, getting nowhere because a vital instruction is missing or misplaced.

At least once that crossword puzzle is solved, the machine itself is fairly reliable. Not so the software. Dr Carl Hammer, who retired in 1981 as director of computer sciences for the American computer company Sperry Univac, believes it may be decades before the maturity of software design matches that of the hardware. These problems come into two stages: the operating systems that tell a computer how to organise its own resources, and the application programs that tell it how to do a particular job. Hammer says that operating systems, particularly for big machines, are plagued with software problems "for which there seem to be few, if any, remedies". Some of those problems can emerge months after the computer has been put to work.

Such frankness is typical of the computer community's corporate assumption of guilt. On applications software, Dr Doug Eyeoins, director-general of Britain's Computing Services Association, says that programming errors are still so commonplace that 60 to 80 per cent of the average programmer's time is spent in fixing programs rather than writing new ones. Other computer scientists have dismissed most programming as a mixture of tried method, rule of thumb and intuition.

These are the main reasons why gas bills for £1,000,000 have arrived at surburban homes, to be followed by computer-generated final demands. It is one aspect of the hoary but sound adage: don't blame the computer, blame the people. The computer is infinitely literal-minded. It cannot (yet) reason for itself; it has to rely on the human programmer to guide it. As the everyday uses of the computer become more complex, so richer analytical talents are required to ensure that we have precisely translated our intentions into computer language, and also covered the odd eventualities which could arise in a computer's work and which could direct it down an overlooked bizarre alley, like sending out a nonsensical gas bill.

Nowadays, those problems are sharpening because the computer is coming out of the closet. Thanks to the chip, it no longer needs air-conditioned temples and technocratic acolytes. It is spreading into the hands of everyman, at the office desk and on the factory bench, and the new users of computers need programs that are not only sound but inherently understandable by an amateur.

At the top, programming requirements are becoming even more complex. Dr Darrel Ince, of the Open University, in bewailing the lack of commercial research here, has pointed out that the business programming that caused computer cock-ups in the past, was usually quite small, a few hundred lines of code written by a few programmers; but projects such as the Space Shuttle and missile defence systems rely on programs containing hundreds of thousands of lines of code, written by teams of hundreds.

At least there is a let-out at the bottom end. This is the software package, the well-tried omnibus program that different firms can use to do the same routine job, like handling the payroll. The recession has encouraged more firms to buy packages rather than waste rare skills in developing their own way of handling business computer tasks. Eyeoins believes that the package will take programming into the surer production-line phase, just as the model T Ford changed the way of making cars.

So much for the technicalities. The human problems of the race into information technology bite deeper — computer crime, invasion of privacy, upheavals in employment and education. Weaving its way through all these issues is an underlying principle that tends to become overshadowed. It is that the silicon chip does not so much present us with novel problems but rather clarifies old ones, forcing us to face absurdities that once we could pretend did not exist. After all, computers are rigidly logical; people are not.

A good example is the story of the robot that failed, through no fault of its own. It failed primarily because it was employed too late to save a 150–year-old factory from death by recession, and secondly because it went to work before its human instructors had learnt the lessons that the robot itself had to teach. This particular robot, a Unimate 2000, joined the Smethwick glassworks of Chance Brothers, part of the Pilkington group, in 1978. It produced radar cones and screens, in a variety of shapes and sizes, for defence equipment, until the factory closed in the spring of 1981.

The original human work was based on one of the oldest industrial skills. An operator lifted molten glass from a furnace at the end of an eight foot long gathering arm. He then rotated and manipulated that molten ball (called a gob) until he knew by long experience that it was the right shape and texture to be put into a mould. At Smethwick, those workers, known as gatherers, were all in their late 50s. The task of handling a heavy gob near a furnace with temperatures of up to 1200 degrees Centigrade was becoming increasingly tough for them. It can take eight years to train a gatherer and few youngsters were daft enough to accept such a long apprenticeship for such an unpleasant job. Therefore, Chance Brothers turned to the robot.

However, it took nearly two years of trial and error to teach it the ritual. First the firm filmed the craftsmen at work and tried to copy exactly what they did. That did not work. Mr Tony Timmins, the company's process manager, explained at the time: "Each gatherer has his own method. Some will be good at one product but produce poorer results with another". The final solution was to give the robot its own more consistent technique — and that meant tightening the whole production chain. A less than perfect quality of glass could be tolerated in the old days, because the gatherers used their experience to pick the best bits.

Therefore, before the robot finally took over, the firm had to ensure that the quality of the glass was uniformly high. However, once those illogicalities had been tackled, the robot worked two shifts a day — the work of eight men — producing 36 varieties of cones and screens. Quality and quantity rose 'considerably'. But to no avail. Demand for the narrow-market products fell and the factory was closed a year later.

The glass-gathering robot of Smethwick is a simple example of many of the lessons of information technology. First, it demonstrates that even the most traditional of industries need to sharpen their reaction times to survive in a world where products and production processes are shorter-lived — and that would be equally true if we were riding on a boom, not caught in a slump.

Secondly, it shows that the computer can work faster and better than people in jobs that previously were thought of as involving human skills requiring long apprenticeships. Other obvious examples are the printer and the draughtsman. However, the argument is wider than that; the role of middle management is threatened by the computer's ability to prepare decision-shaping information for top management. (One American office-automation company has mischievously forecast that top management will also be threatened eventually — because the mystique of management will be exploded once information flows electronically round a company in all directions, instead of safely from top to bottom).

Thirdly, the Smethwick robot shows that the logic of automation can force firms to face inefficiencies that were hidden before. On this point Whitehall itself has yet to practise what it preaches.

Since 1978 (and that was woefully late), successive British Governments have been berating industry to embrace the microchip with the fervour of the Japanese, in order to save ourselves from becoming the first de-industrialised nation. The latest version is the Dalek-echoing phrase of the Information Technology Minister, Mr Kenneth Baker: "Automate or liquidate". Yet not only is information technology comparatively little used in central government, there is also an old-world division of responsibility for information technology between the Home Office and the Department of Industry. Some top civil servants say that this is a good thing, because when information technology does become nationally pervasive, it would be dangerous to have such political power concentrated in one corner. There is tentative evidence to support them in the way that divided views are slowing the plan to make Britain a 'wired society' on a basis of local cable television monopolies — a basis which might, at the outset, kill the heady prospect of open access to the new electronic media.

Nevertheless, the Home Office — despite yelps of anguish from the Department of Industry — has been alarmingly slow in updating the law to meet the changes wrought by information technology. Central issues are how — if at all — copyright can be preserved in computer software; whether information is itself a 'thing' that can be stolen; why we have so few police officers skilled in the intricacies of computer-related crime; but, above all, how the citizen should be protected against the misuse of personal information held in computers.

The key word here is correlation. Many campaigners for civil liberties say that computerisation of personal records does not bring a change in principle: what matters is the collecting of private information on individuals in any form, whether by government departments or commercial concerns. Once such information is in a computer system, the change in scope is so enormous that points of principle become pedantic. Items previously held on paper and stuffed into filing cabinets in several different government or company departments, can be correlated into a comprehensive dossier at a speed and to a depth that would have been inconceivable before.

If a modern society — wedded to plastic money, computer-based travel and hotel booking networks, computer-read passports, and uncorsetted police and bureaucratic databanks — had no legal constraints on the gathering and use of personal information, then it could make Orwell's version of 1984 look like Liberty Hall. In such a real 1984 it would be possible, by punching a few keys on a computer terminal, to tell where, when, and how you travelled, whether by car, plane or train; where you stayed (and who was with you); what you said on the telephone; what your doctor thinks of your liver; and what the local police sergeant thinks of your family life.

A dozen Western nations now have data privacy laws to curtail such possibilities, but Britain is still not among them at the time of writing. The legislation that the Government is at last pondering is to be based on voluntary principles. It will not therefore meet even the modest suggestions of the Lindop committee, which recommended to the Home Secretary in 1978 a statutory data protection authority and enforceable codes of practice. The greatest concern expressed by Lindop was about the police use of computers to correlate criminal intelligence information. Scotland Yard refused to give that official inquiry any information about its criminal intelligence system, which is now believed to hold speculative data concerning nearly 1,500,000 people, many of them, of course, having no criminal records. Lindop's verdict was harsh:

"While we have no reason to believe that the public need be unduly alarmed by the general use of computers for police purposes, in relation to the Metropolitan Police we do not have enough evidence to give a firm assurance to that effect."

Another source of immediate concern is the increasing exchange of computer data between nations. As we have seen, information can now be sent so quickly and comparatively cheaply by telephone line and satellite that the location of computers is becoming irrelevant to the work they do. Lindop said that if British data protection legislation was long delayed, the UK could become a 'data haven', a refuge for companies wanting to dodge legal restrictions in other countries. The issue also worries trade unions because of the way in which multi-national companies can switch work around the world.

Mr Jan Freese, director-general of the Swedish Data Inspection Board (Sweden was the first nation to enact data privacy laws in 1973), calls it "sunshine computing" because companies move work from continent to continent, following the sun and the office hours in different countries. Mr Freese is a firm advocate of the wide adoption of the European convention on privacy to counter 'data havens'.

Britain has said that she will ratify the European convention and that provides a ray of hope about minimal British legislation: for the convention prohibits the collection of data about a person's race, religion or politics except under safeguards.

However, such issues become subordinate in most people's minds when compared with the central social problem of the spread of information technology: jobs. The examples I have given show, I think, that the computer tends to take over the middleman jobs, reducing the human intervention between the originator of a product or service and the customer who uses it; and that eventually some advisory professionals could become redundant middlemen as much as the semi-skilled worker tied to a factory production line. In short, greater wealth can be produced from fewer but more highly-skilled people.

Here is another example among the many. The telecommunications industry is expanding because of the wider opportunities the chip has brought in computerised communications. However, in many areas, it is cutting employment as it expands. The people who go are those with what they imagined to be lifetime skills in the old methods of making and running telephone exchanges and related equipment. The demand now is for smaller numbers of much more highly paid people, qualified in computer programming and microelectronic engineering. The change can be illustrated by one statistic: one microchip in the newer, faster teleprinters replaces 900 parts that had to be assembled in the old machines. So: fewer people are needed to make teleprinters, and fewer to maintain them.

But that is just a sharp acceleration of a process of industrial automation that has been underway for decades, one cause of the shift in employment from manufacturing to service industries. The real point is that those new teleprinters are likely to have a much shorter lifetime than their predecessors. Many of them could be replaced —perhaps within five to six years — by communicating desk-top computers, voice controlled, through which the boss will be able to dictate, edit, then send letters and messages directly.

That will cut employment in many areas — fewer typists, postmen, teleprinter operators, messengers, clerks, printers, even fewer lumber-jacks and paper-mill workers; and, as we have seen, the process does not stop there; middle management, the professions and service trades, such as shopkeeping and travel agencies, could come next.

The response to this challenge by most politicians and economists, whether of Left or Right, is to point to the historical evidence (which is indeed impressive) and to say the equation that has worked so far —new technology equals new wealth, equals new demand, equals new jobs — will still apply. Most of them admit, however, that this will now happen at a greater rate than before and that many people will have to retrain for several different careers in a lifetime. Also, the historical process of shorter working weeks and earlier retirement should gather corresponding pace.

However there is a minority view, expounded again on both Left and Right. This says that for once history could be bunk, because now that we have the first universal machine (a machine that finally fulfils computer science theory by being capable of performing any task we can precisely define), the new areas of mass employment it could create to replace the old could themselves quickly become automated as well. Therefore this school argue that, recession apart, millions more could be without economic work in Britain by the 1990s. But that, they say, need not mean unemployment, if we are prepared to remould the Protestant work ethic, concentrate on creating wealth rather than jobs and use that greater wealth to organise richer opportunities for recreation, education and public service.

Such a massive social reorganisation is required, they say, to prevent society dividing even more perilously between the haves and the have-nots, between a technocratic information-rich elite and the information-poor. This school is not dismayed by the medical and social science evidence that unemployment can be a carrier of disease, as well as a generator of riots, through its destruction of self-esteem. They reply that the reality of the work ethic would be retained in the new opportunities to serve others to do real work. All that would go would be the outmoded basic link between work and economic reward. Those who love the rat race could still soldier on.

Over fanciful, maybe — not to say over-optimistic about man's humanity to man — but at least the urgency of public debate on these issues is shown by one vital point of agreement on both sides of the argument. This is that in a competitive world there is no alternative to using the chip as quickly and as widely as possible if we still want a Western lifestyle of washing machines, colour television and Mediterranean holidays. If the people of any one nation do decide to cling to jobs that are no longer necessary — and indeed, may have become literally counter-productive — then they must also be prepared to be poor.

In the spring of 1979, just before the general election, public debate was indeed beginning, only to be stifled first by the election campaign, then by recession. Now it is trickling back. Some. leading Conservatives at that time joined with Leftish union leaders, like Mr Clive Jenkins, in arguing that full employment could never return and that we should think of new ways of distributing wealth — by whatever political means. Mr James Prior, new Northern Ireland Secretary, spoke in this way. So did Mr Peter Walker, the Agriculture Minister, and he still does.

Walker has said that our attitude to automation verges on the lunatic. "We should rejoice and create a society in which the machine works 24 hours a day... Uniquely in history we have the circumstances in which we can create Athens without the slaves." The next generation would not be satisfied, he said, by guarantees that they could work in factory, mine, or boring office for 50 years of their lives. There was an urgent need to develop a new approach to employment in which the benefits of technology were used for all, to provide a fuller life.

Such brave words, essentially echoed today by Mr Len Murray, of the TUC, demonstrate that the work issue is not essentially a party political one (a national basic wage could be organised under any ideology) but a struggle between radicals of many persuasions and the deeper conservative power structures, industrial as well as political, Left as well as Right. If the traditionalists win, it is not fanciful to forecast that the century-long horrors of the first Industrial Revolution (which gave us eventually common luxuries that once the rich could only dream about) might be repeated — but crushed into two decades at most.

That is the real challenge of information technology: to stop history repeating itself, so that our children reap the benefits, not just our great grand-children. For one education-rationed generation it is already perilously late.

2

Here and Now

ALAN CANE

The Financial Times

CUSTOMERS seeking an overdraft, a mortgage or simply advice about their financial affairs come face to face dramatically with information technology at National Westminster Bank's Surbiton, Surrey, branch.

Their interview with Mr David Reygate, the branch manager, follows the traditional pattern — with a major difference.

His desk is virtually free of paper. He may make notes as the interview proceeds, but the bulky, dog-eared file containing the records of all the customer's dealings with the bank and which all managers have to consult to bring themselves up-to-date, is conspicuously absent.

Instead, Mr Reygate has a low, neat keyboard in front of him. At his right elbow sits a large grey television set to which he makes frequent reference.

Mr Reygate is among the first of a new generation of bank managers who have begun to make use of information technology in the routine course of their work. All his customer records are held in the memory of a computer situated in the machine room of the branch.

At the touch of a key, he can call any record to his own screen for perusal or modification. What is happening in Surbiton today will be commonplace in every bank branch tomorrow.

If Surbiton sounds an unlikely place to find a leading edge of information technology, Mr Reygate has discovered that his customers are not overawed by their 'electronic bank manager'.

"Many of the companies in this area are involved in the electronics or computer business", he points out. "They see nothing surprising about it at all."

———————————

Edward Wilson and Son of Liverpool has been making superb machinery for the leather trade for over 100 years. Its speciality is the large spiral knives which are used to flesh, scour and unhair hides prior to tanning.

The trade press of the time said of a machine it launched in 1882: "It is never bigoted, drunk, tired or lazy … an unskilled labourer or boy will do the work of from eight to ten workers".

Two years ago, the three great grandsons of the founder of the firm put their own contribution to the automation of leather processing on the market.

It was designed to solve the tanner's most intractable problem: they buy hides by weight in a wet and hairy state, but sell the dyed and polished finished product by area. The new machine measures the area of the raw hides using photoelectric techniques; special sensors measure the thickness. The results enable the tanner to decide how to get the most out of each hide.

It all used to be done by skilled human sorters. Wilson's device has added numeracy to what had been an art and craft. As Mr Raymond Wilson, the company's joint managing director put it pithily: "This machine tells the tanner for the first time what the hell is going on in his own factory".

A tannery in Hull, Holmes Hall, took the first of the machines. It paid for itself in a matter of months.

Wilson and Son has a fine track record in innovation; and it did its reputation justice with the new machine. It was among the first to take advantage of a Government campaign to encourage the use of microelectronic technology in industrial products and it was among the first to use an advanced kind of computer memory — bubble memory — that is particularly suited to the rough and dirty conditions of the shop floor.

———————————

Mr Colin Crook, a British veteran of the semiconductor business, and Mr Harry Saal are respectively chief executives of the sister companies Zynar and Nestar.

The two companies, both of which specialise in ways of giving business executives personal computer power, work closely together and operate a joint research and development department. Not unnaturally, Mr Crook and Mr Saal talk together a lot; almost as much as Mr Crook and his technical manager, Ian Powers.

However the desks of Mr Crook and Mr Powers are separated by only 10 yards at Zynar's Uxbridge, Middlesex, headquarters. Mr Saal at Nestar is 5000 miles distant in California. How do they communicate? Well, there is always the telephone, but the inevitable time difference between London and California allows only a one hour 'window' in the late afternoon when the two business days are in phase. So on his desk, Mr Crook has a microcomputer, an Apple II as it happens. So does Mr Saal and Mr Powers and everybody else in the Zynar and Nestar companies. They write letters on the screens of their computers, and at a touch of a key, the letter is sent over the telephone network to its intended recipient.

It is called 'electronic mail'. It combines the advantages of the telephone — speed and individuality — with those of conventional mail, a full and detailed text and the fact that the recipient does not have to be physically at his or her address for delivery to take place. In fact, the recipient does not even have to look at his incoming electronic mail until it is convenient for him to do so. The Zynar/Nestar version of electronic mail includes the capacity for word processing. Colin Crook says: "Nobody writes memoranda in this company. We only have two typewriters between the lot of us and we're hoping to get rid of those".

He also points out: "How many chief executives have a computer on their desks — and use it?"

These three examples show some of the very different ways in which information technology is transforming business and personal life. But even if a senior Zynar executive said of his company's electronic mail system: "We could not run the organisation without it", the fact is that bankers kept adequate customer records, the tanning industry produced high quality leathers and international companies sent telex messages between their subsidiaries in different continents long before the term 'information technology' became common currency.

Yet banking is being turned upside down by modern technology. At present, customers travel to their bank branches where their accounts are managed by bank staff.

Before very long, customers will do their own banking in the privacy of their own homes using television sets and keyboards just like Mr Reygate's.

The whole of manufacturing industry is going through drastic reappraisal as robot systems and manufacturing cells are brought in on an ever increasing scale to create factories where human workers have no place. Fujitsu Fanuc, the Japanese company which is the world's largest manufacturer of computers to control machine tools, has a factory in the shadow of Mount Fuji where industrial robots controlled by computers make other industrial robots. Humans are not needed except for administration and minor machine adjustments. By 1985, the factory will employ only 200 people, about one tenth the number required in conventional plants of similar capacity.

Conventional factories are set up with production lines geared to high rates of production of a particular part, component or whole product. Factories like Fujitsu Fanuc's, based on information technology, can be turned easily to the manufacture of a different product simply by reprogramming the computers controlling the industrial robots.

Smaller manufacturers in Japan are able to rent or lease industrial robots which they set to making their products automatically while they practice their swing on the local golf course.

In the office, traditional skills are becoming redundant. Secretaries need no longer be able to spell; their electronic typewriters or word processors automatically make corrections.

The need for high quality artists and draughtsmen is being eroded by computers which can be used by the unskilled to produce charts and diagrams on television screens in a multitude of colours. When the executive is satisfied with his or her handiwork, the resulting image can be printed out on paper for binding into a report or as a slide for formal presentations.

Even specialists such as accountants and statisticians are at risk. There is a growing trend for small businessmen to buy small computers to handle their stock control, invoicing and accounting. There is an equally strong trend for senior company executives to buy small computers to analyse the development of their businesses and make projections for the years ahead.

By now it must be apparent that information technology possesses at least two very special qualities. It can be used in a very wide spectrum of human activities and its use tends to change those activities out of all recognition.

Why should this be? What gives this technology its special power to influence virtually every aspect of our lives?

The answer has two dimensions. First, computer techniques are used to reduce all information to a common language. Second, the development of silicon based semiconductor manufacturing methods has brought the price of information technology within the reach of almost every area of human endeavour.

The common language which unites all facets of information technology today is the binary code.

Used by all digital computers, it represents all forms of information, numbers, text, images, sounds, colours, by various combinations of only two quantities, the first representing 'power off' in a computer circuit, the second representing 'power on'. Conventionally, the 'power off' state is represented by the number 0, the 'power on' state by the number 1. (In commercial computers, 0 and 1 may refer to high voltage and 0 to low voltage, but the principle is the same: only two states are used in the code, and there are no intermediate steps between the state corresponding to a 0 and the state corresponding to a 1).

These 0s and 1s are called binary digits, or bits for short, and they make counting very simple for electronic computers. Their circuits can be arranged to add, subtract or compare strings of electronic impulses which in turn represent numbers, letters or perhaps a particular part of a diagram.

However if binary code is very convenient from the point of view of the electronic digital computer, it has even more significance and importance to information technology.

Once a piece of information has been captured in binary form, it can be stored, retrieved, manipulated and transmitted without risk of alteration or degradation.

Consider, for example, a conventional telephone call. Speech is transmitted along the copper telephone wire as a continuously varying electrical signal — an analogue of the voice pattern. It is subject to interference, to cross talk and to accidental alteration each time the signal is boosted by repeaters as it goes on its way. In short, the signal which eventually arrives at the far end of the line may be a very poor analogue of the original speech.

Now the analogue signal generated in a telephone handset by the human voice can be converted into digital signals — into binary code —by techniques in which the signal is measured at predetermined points and the resulting numerical value converted to binary code. With these methods, the voice is transmitted down the wire as a stream of electronic pulses, corresponding to a pattern of 0s and 1s. The receiving station will *only* recognise a pulse of electricity or the absence of one. Nothing in between is allowed, and the information can be divided into groups of bits with correction codes added to ensure that a group of bits which arrives at the receiving station, is the same group of bits which started the journey.

But, and this is very important, voice messages are not the only kind of information which can be turned into bits and transmitted along a telephone cable; television, facsimile, photographs and computer data can all be reduced to the same series of electronic pulses and transmitted without degradation anywhere on Earth. Or in deep space, for that matter.

Existing telephone systems have limited capacity to deal with digital signalling because copper wire and existing telephone exchanges are best suited to handle electrical analogues of the spoken word. However most of the world's telecommunications authorities (called the PTTs, standing for Post, Telephone and Telecommunications authorities) are planning to install digital exchanges, followed by digital networks.

There is also much excitement about the prospect of replacing the copper cabling which constitutes the present telephone network with glass fibre pipes, bundles of pure glass fibres thinner than a human hair. The glass used is of such purity that a block 12 miles thick would still be as transparent as a window pane.

A network of glass fibre would not carry electrical signals, but pulses of light injected into the cable using tiny but powerful lasers. Glass fibre cables have many times the capacity of copper cables for carrying digital information. For transmitting large volumes of information between continents, communications satellites have the greatest potential for voice, data and image.

The *Financial Times*, for example, prints both in London and Frankfurt. The Frankfurt edition, specially tuned to overseas markets is prepared in London and facsimile images sent electronically to the Frankfurt printers using perhaps the most sophisticated, high quality system in Europe.

Each page is scanned by a special machine which records in digital form the entire image of the page. It compresses the number of bits needed to map out each page by ignoring the pink areas between the black lettering. Clever computer techniques are needed to reconstruct the original page from the stream of bits which arrive in Frankfurt over a leased telecommunications line.

As the Royal Wedding was making history in late 1981, British Telecom engineers were making history of a different sort as they fixed a medium sized dish antennae to the roof of the *Financial Times* building in the shadow of St Pauls Cathedral to beam images of the FT pages to Frankfurt via a communications satellite.

That was simply a trial, the first example of remote printing in Europe, but for several weeks, signals were sent daily to West Germany proving without doubt that transmission of information for printing by satellite is possible and has advantages in speed, cost and accuracy over land line systems.

Another indication of the power of the common language of information technology is given by the Mitsui trading company, one of Japan's major and longest established organisations. Its world wide communications network already handles about one million messages a month. To improve the efficiency with which it communicates with its overseas operations, it has recently linked optical character recognition equipment to its telex and message switching centres.

Telex is the oldest form of electronic mail and enables companies with a teleprinter to send a typed message to another teleprinter. The constraints are the same, the recipient's teleprinter has to be switched on and free to receive the incoming call.

Message switching systems make it possible to send telexes automatically. Basically a message switch is simply a computer which *stores* telex messages sent from one teleprinter and *forwards* them to another, designated teleprinter when it is free. These days teleprinters are being replaced with devices looking more like computer terminals with screens and keyboards. It is much easier to prepare and edit a message on a screen-based terminal compared to an old fashioned teleprinter.

What Mitsui did was to take the problem of putting information easily into its message switching system a step further. Machines already exist which can 'read' certain kinds of typescript. Mitsui staff simply type their messages on paper then feed them to one of these optical character readers, as they are called. The machine reads the text, converts it into digital form and transmits it directly to the company's message switching centre. Mr S. Sato, Mitsui's London Communications Manager says that London alone now handles 1400 messages a day with just five operators working in three shifts.

What if an optical character reader should fail to recognise a letter? Does that make nonsense of the whole technology?

The common language of the binary code offers a simple solution. Some modern optical character recognition devices can operate in two ways — as a conventional OCR machine or as a facsimile machine. So if the machine is reading a text and comes across a character it cannot recognise and so translate into binary code, it switches itself into a facsimile machine and simply records the image of that character — to the machine it is all just a stream of binary digits.

A further example of the universal nature of information once it has been translated into binary code comes from the printing industry. Full colour pictures in books and magazines are produced by an elaborate process in which the original photograph is rephotographed through coloured screens to separate out the four basic printing colours, cyan, magenta, black and yellow.

Each of these monotone photographs is used to make a separate printing plate, and the original coloured image is recreated on the page by printing the four colours, one on top of each other.

It is time consuming, skilled and expensive work. Crosfield Electronics, part of the De La Rue group, has won several Queen's Awards for Technological Achievement, the last in 1981, for the development of a machine which can produce the four colour separations needed to make the printing plates in one pass.

The Crosfield machine determines the colour composition of the photograph on a single pass using optical techniques and stores the information in binary code.

Not only is it quick and easy to use the stored information to create the printing plates, but because it is in binary code, the language computers understand, it can be manipulated at will.

The entire photograph can be displayed on a television screen; if the artist feels the colours are not quite right, he can change them by touching a few keys. If the complexion of a model's face is less than perfect, he can electronically airbrush the blemishes away.

There is, in fact, no need to begin with nature in the production of pictures and images by computer. The most advanced visual display screens, these days, have such fine resolution that an artist can build up a half-tone 'photograph' point by point which is indistinguishable from the real thing.

For the future, this raises awkward philosophical questions about the veracity of published and broadcast images. What would one make, for example, of a television 'soap opera' produced cartoon-fashion without actors or production team by a team of animators and scriptwriters seated at keyboards with television screens to capture the results of their work. To the computer and its display system, there is no difference between a stream of bits representing the image of a real person and a stream of bits conjured up on a keyboard.

For the present, advanced computer images are making possible the training of air pilots and oil rig operators in simulators at only a fraction of the price of the real thing.

Modern aeroplane simulators are a far cry from the old 'Link' trainers which gave prospective pilots a first taste of their future working environment four decades ago.

Simulators built by organisations such as Rediffusion are exact replicas of the cockpits of the big jets. Their 'windows' are television screens displaying computer generated images of what the pilot could expect to see landing his airliner at London Heathrow, Paris Charles de Gaulle or New York Kennedy airports. The images are uncannily accurate. Simulation of a night landing is virtually indistinguishable from the real thing. It has to be. The cost of running a big airliner is now so exorbitant that aircrew these days can expect to carry out virtually all their training in simulators. Simulation is now used extensively to train helicopter pilots, naval crews and even oil rig operators. It simply costs less to run a simulator than an aeroplane, ship or rig.

So we have now seen that information of all sorts has a common language in the binary code and that computer technology offers a common means of carrying out transactions in that language. That is why information technology is so all-pervasive. But it does not explain why information technology has suddenly taken on so much new significance. After all, the binary system has been known and understood by mathematicians for centuries. Digital computers employing binary arithmetic and binary logic have been in existence since the mid 1940s.

What has changed has been the cost of computing power.

Computing power has become unbelievably cheaper over the past two decades as a direct result of startling developments in the electronics and semiconductor industries, which have made it possible to create entire computers on tiny slivers of silicon — *and to mass produce these at very low cost.*

A modern computer can be thought of as carefully planned assemblage of switches each of which can be either 'on' or 'off', which can either allow an electrical signal to proceed or impede its progress. In early computers, these switches were built up of thermionic valves, large, expensive, fragile and with a healthy appetite for electrical power.

What many consider to be the major invention of the century occurred in December 1947 at Bell Laboratories in New Jersey, U.S.A. John Bardeen, Walter Brattain and William Shockley built a device they called the 'transistor' from semiconducting materials which performed like valves. Transistors were tiny, cheap to make *en masse*, rugged, consumed little power and gave out little heat. The invention of the transistor made possible modern information technology.

From the transistor it was only a short step, conceptually speaking, to the integrated circuit, the fabrication of an entire electronic circuit complete with transistors, resistors and so on, on a small chip of semiconducting material, silicon. It was a very long step in terms of research effort; the patent for the first integrated circuit was filed by Mr Jack Kilby of the US electronics company Texas Instruments in 1959, over a decade after the triumphant announcement of the transistor from Bell Laboratories. This made possible miniaturisation on a remarkable scale. The first integrated circuits contained only a few components. For example, most on/off switches in the microcircuit are called 'gates'. Small scale integrated circuits of the earliest type contained about 10 gates; there followed medium scale integration with about 30 gates per chip, large scale integration with some 100 gates per chip and the semiconductor industry is now moving to very large scale integration with more than 1000 gates on each chip.

Information technology depends on two types of microchip; first, the microprocessor in which the arithmetical and logical functions of an entire computer are squeezed down onto a quarter inch square of silicon, and the solid state memory chip. Memory chips today can store 64,000 individual binary digits, but within the foreseeable future as many as one million bits will be stored on a single one.

It is already possible to fabricate an entire computer — arithmetical and logic functions, memory and the necessary circuits to allow the computer to communicate with the outside world — on a single piece of silicon.

However the real secret of the microcomputer revolution is cost — in the early days of computing, the physical elements of the computer —the hardware — were so expensive that the machines were applied only to information recognised as having high value; military and government data for example.

Microprocessors and solid state memories can be made literally for *pence*, so their range of applications is much wider. They start life as a block of ultra pure silicon which is sliced into circular wafers about 10 centimetres in diameter and 0.5 millimetres in thickness. Each wafer now goes through a complex series of steps at the end of which it will have between 200 and 300 individual devices — processors or memories — constructed on it. The process is called photolithography

— writing on stone using light. A chemical which is sensitive to light is applied to the wafer and then a photographic image of the circuit required is projected onto the wafer. The unexposed parts of the pattern are then washed off the wafer and chemicals which improve silicon's ability to function as a semiconductor are etched or diffused into the surface of the silicon.

This finicky, difficult process is repeated until the required circuit pattern is complete. The wafer is then tested automatically to isolate bad chips before being scribed and broken apart to yield individual chips 2.5 to 7.5 millimetres square. It is easy to describe; very difficult to do. Yields of good chips can be quite low. Every so often a chip plant goes through an unexplained trauma in which none of the chips it makes are perfect.

When the production lines are running well, millions of chips can be fabricated at very low cost.

For the future, manufacturers are looking to new fabrication techniques in which beams of electrons or X-rays will be used to 'write' directly on the chip surface. There is some excitement about a material called gallium arsenide which promises, for some applications at least, to give rise to microprocessors which work even faster than those fabricated in silicon. There is also a lot of research going into 'Josephson junctions' based on the way materials behave at temperatures close to absolute zero and which promise the fastest computers of all.

It would not be fair, however, to discuss the quite dramatic reductions in both the size and the cost of computer machinery without mentioning the thorny problem of software. The physical machinery of the computer is the hardware, the lists of instructions which make the computer work and which make it possible for computers to do anything from accountancy and payroll to brewing is the software.

Digital computers are distinguished by the fact that their software is stored away in their memory along with all the data necessary for their allotted tasks.

Good accurate software is difficult to write. Computers are literal-minded beasts and anything less than a completely accurate instruction leads it to make a nonsense of its job. This book contains several thousand sentences. Imagine having to write and print a book this size without making any grammatical or literal errors, and you will have some idea of the problems of producing a sizeable computer program.

The kind of people who can carry out this exacting and detailed work are scarce, which is why software is expensive. Software 'factories', where computers write programs for other computers, special programs which make it easier for the unskilled software writer to write good programs, and 'software packages' generalised programs written for specific applications — payroll, for example — which can be used without modification by many users, are some of the ways the computer industry is exploring to hold the cost of software to reasonable levels. As one American semiconductor company executive remarked of his latest super chip: "This could be the first chip that costs five dollars to buy and a million dollars to program!"

It is all very well to discuss the hardware and software of information technology — what does it mean in the real world of business, commerce and industry?

It has to be admitted that the devices we use to communicate with microchips are primitive in scope and flexibility compared with such traditional tools like paper and pencil.

Manufacturers provide keyboards to write instructions to the computer and television-like screens (monitors) to see the machine's response because that is the best the technology can offer today and for the foreseeable future.

Everybody agrees that equipment that you could speak to in English and which could talk back would be a great leap forward, and there are spectacular developments in this area. At Texas Instrument's Bedford, England, plant, staff gain admission to the main research facility by announcing themselves to a microphone at the door.

The microphone is linked to a computer, which asks them to wait while it checks their voiceprint against authorised samples in its memory. If it finds a match it opens the door. The computer generated voice is remarkably lifelike; those who have used Texas Instruments *Speak and Spell* learning aid will know what a chip talking sounds like. Voice generation, in fact, is very well established. IBM has produced a typewriter for the blind which reads out what has been typed. Now it has adapted this technology to build a computer terminal for the blind. It has a screen — which sounds like a nonsense — but it also tells the operator, in spoken English, what has been typed on that screen.

Persuading computers to recognise and 'understand' human speech is more difficult, but already some advanced products have a limited kind of speech recognition facility built in. Calma, a Californian company that builds machines to put the power of the computer at the elbow of the designer (more about this in Ron Jackson's chapter) launched a machine that responds to simple operator commands like 'zoom' or 'move right'. Its vocabulary is 50 words long and it only needs to 'hear' a word three times to be sure of responding to its operator's voice. Given that it will be some years before we can converse with a computer as easily as with another human being, the chief means of communication between man and system is going to be the computer terminal.

In the early days, that is all it was; the far end of a communication line from a computer. These days it will have its own microprocessor and memory built in, probably function quite satisfactorily without being connected to a computer and carry out a number of distinct functions.

At its most advanced, the humble computer terminal becomes the office workstation. The idea is that the visual display screen and keyboard should combine and replace completely all the conventional tools of the office. So there will be no need for a typewriter — the work-station will be equipped for word processing. There will be no need for filing cabinets. The work-station will be connected to a very large memory with clever software to ensure that any piece of information can be retrieved rapidly.

The screen may even replace the desk top itself. Some researchers are working on a screen which will give a visual image of a desk top complete with books and papers which can be shuffled electronically.

Some manufacturers have produced commercial terminals which go some way down this road by providing tiny images of filing cabinets and so on on the screen or providing keys on the keyboard specially labelled 'in tray' and 'out tray'. Some have a key labelled 'wastebin' which consigns information to an electronic limbo for 24 hours then destroys it.

Some screens are touch sensitive; some can be written on with an 'electronic pencil'. And some manufacturers have built machines with a 'mouse', a box of tricks which can be moved around the desk top to move the cursor on the screen in an identical manner.

All these work-stations, electronic memories and printing devices will be connected together so that people can talk to each other over their desk telephones or send each other memos through the electronic mail system.

Special techniques called local area networking are being devised to link all information technology machines on a single site cheaply and effectively.

So manufacturers are trying to mould their products so they are better suited to the humans who will use them and the tasks to which they will be put. At some future date our present efforts to communicate with machines will seem laughably primitive — but that date is a long way off.

What can be learned from information technology in action? First, companies with a record of innovation and management with a forward looking attitude make the best of the advantages of information technology. Lansing Bagnall, the fork-lift truck manufacturer, bought a robot to automate the wiring on its trucks. It did the necessary modifications itself so successfully that the firm is now thinking of going into the automation business.

Second, it is still very early days. Very few companies are using the new information technology; those that are are learning more from their mistakes than their successes. And the technology itself has a long way to go.

The all-pervasive nature of information technology based on binary code and cheap hardware means that progress is being made simultaneously on many fronts. Most information technologists agree that predictions of when the technology will reach a certain stage are often decades too pessimistic.

In the second part of this book, experts from a number of different disciplines will describe how information technology is moulding their working lives — and what it holds for the future.

Part Two

3

An Application of Information Technology in Engineering Design

R H JACKSON

CAE Manager, Baker Perkins Ltd, Peterborough

BAKER PERKINS LTD is the senior company of a U.K. based international group which has been established for many years as a supplier of machinery to several process industries. As a leading manufacturer of bakery machinery, the company supplies unit machines and plant for a wide variety of bread, roll and cake production. These products range from sophisticated dough mixing and handling systems to large, fully automatic ovens which will bake over 4000 loaves an hour. Much of this equipment is under microelectronic control. The company is also the market leader for the supply of complete lines of biscuit making machinery, over 80 per cent of which is exported. The majority of the nationally known brands are made on Baker Perkins plant. Chocolate and confectionery equipment is also supplied to a world-wide market. Much use is made of standard machine modules but each item of plant is tailored to the individual customer's specific requirements. There is a general similarity of shape and style running through the range of machine designs which have to satisfy stringent standards of safety and hygiene.

Although of heavier construction and engineered to particularly exacting standards of precision, the company's very successful web-offset, heat-set litho colour printing presses also have similar characteristics of component shape. This diverse range of equipment indicates the wide scope of the design activity within the organisation.

The design of successful machinery for these markets requires knowledge and experience of both product and process as well as careful attention to production engineering. With such a high level of export sales, about two thirds of the total, it is essential that cycle time is kept to a minimum through all stages of the contract from initial enquiry to commissioning and after-sales service. These pressures must not be allowed to interfere with the innovation of new products to tight market specifications.

A few statistics may help to illustrate the problems of management and production control. About 10,000 new drawings are produced annually together with 10,000 sheets of parts lists. In the factory the average component batch size is three and some 100,000 batches of parts are produced annually. There are approximately 500,000 items in the inventory.

Over the years the company has tackled the fundamental problems of 'jobbing shop' production with great vigour. In the years after the 1939–45 war much attention was given to introducing well-chosen standards and means of reducing the range of inventory items without inhibiting design. Among the management aids introduced was the Brisch coding system for materials, commodities and standard components. With this degree of organisation it was a natural step twenty years ago to introduce computer technology. Since those days of relatively primitive computer operations a comprehensive main-frame computer system has been established. Initially installed for inventory and production control, the facilities have been developed steadily and interactive parts-listing and process planning systems have been in use for several years. These activities continue to expand and link together so that most of the purchasing function, production control and a large part of the production engineering task are in the hands of a number of highly skilled and experienced staff working interactively with the computer data-base. Much of this work has been designed and developed within the company and represents a very good example of the application of information technology in its own right. This background of experience, with technical management and staff in daily working contact with various computer systems, provided fertile ground for the introduction of CAD/CAM (computer aided design/ computer aided manufacture).

This was the scenario when CAD was first considered in 1976 as a means of reducing the routine and onerous draughting load, freeing engineers for more creative tasks and minimising the cycle time of design and drawing work. Although the manual draughting operation was relatively efficient it was felt that CAD could be worthwhile. Investigation showed that drawing board work accounted for about 30 per cent of the total design and draughting time. The remainder of the time being taken up with tasks such as calculations, tests and trials, communications with other departments, searching for information and parts-listing as well as the creative aspects of design. Nevertheless, it was considered that CAD could be of benefit and serious investigation began with the formation of a working party in December 1976. The working party was chaired by the technical director. The membership consisted of the technical managers of each product division and production engineering, the computer department manager, the software development manager and an engineer with wide knowledge of the work of the drawing offices as secretary. The working party was set a tight time limit and given the task of finding out if a suitable CAD system was available which could be financially justified. This remit was more specific than the brief frequently given to many teams charged with investigating CAD who often have much less management experience. The group quickly reduced the field to a few potential suppliers and laid down a number of basic requirements, which still stand today:

a. *A turn-key system* — to consume a minimum of resources during installation and initial development.
b. *Practical software* — suitable for general mechanical draughting and design with fast response, capable of development and expansion and interfacing with existing company systems (manual and computer-based).

c. *Reliability* — the hardware and software well-proven and able to operate consistently with a minimum of maintenance.

d. *Productivity* — we felt this to be the vital factor. The potential for high productivity should be demonstrated in practical use on work similar to our own.

e. *CAD/CAM capability* — early in our investigations we realised the importance of this essential link to allow exploitation of these techniques from design right through to production.

f. *A 'transparent' system* — to enable the mechanical engineer, without computer experience, to carry out his work effectively on the system with a minimum of interface problems. That is, the system needed to be particularly 'user friendly'.

g. *Competitive price* — the system needed to be economic as a development project through the learning curve and yield a satisfactory return on the investment when fully operational.

Following an intensive period of investigation, including visits to the United States to assess prospective vendors and their products on their home territory, we chose UNIGRAPHICS which is supplied by the McDonnell Douglas Automation Company. The order for our first four-terminal CAD/CAM system was placed in mid-February 1977. The equipment was installed in four days and produced drawings on March 31 — seven weeks later. It was the first system of its kind outside North America.

From the outset it was agreed that the equipment would be situated within the drawing office and run by the engineers with the computer staff in a support role if required. This was a significant factor in gaining the confidence and enthusiasm of the drawing office staff.

Prior to delivery the first group of CAD operators was selected and received a week of training in California. Quite deliberately a typical cross-section of staff was chosen as a test case. Since the first training period all training has been carried out by our own staff in house. Over one hundred and twenty people were trained in the first two years and the total number trained is now over one hundred and sixty. Almost without exception everyone has completed training satisfactorily within four weeks. It is usual for productive drawing work to begin after the first week. The two senior men of the original squad responded particularly well to CAD work and became very efficient system supervisors with wide responsibilities for training, system performance, house-keeping and terminal allocation and loading. It should be mentioned that the majority of their time is spent on productive work although there are no computer operating staff.

The second four terminal CAD system was installed in late 1977. Then, in 1978, the first two systems were increased to six terminals each and a third four terminal system was introduced. Currently a major equipment up-date and expansion is being installed because of the success of CAD/CAM and the heavy demand for additional terminal time. We were indebted to the Department of Industry for their encouragement and grant aid towards a percentage of the capital cost of the first system and, subsequently, a grant towards the development of CAD/CAM procedures.

The hardware, which currently consists of Data General Eclipse 230 computers, 96 megabyte disc drives, Tektronix Model 4014 storage-tube graphics screens and Calcomp 960 plotters, continues to prove remarkably reliable. The software has proved very simple to operate and has functioned efficiently over the full range of our requirements from design layout work through to programming of numerical control machine tools. Although the software has extensive 3-D capability this is little used in practice. Nearly all the work is effectively carried out in 2-D mode.

After five years of operation over half the company's new drawings — 5500 in 1981 mostly A0 and A1 size — are produced on the CAD system as well as over 1000 numerical control programmes each year. Practically all the jig and tool draughting work is committed to CAD. The terminals are operated from six in the morning until late in the evening and, in 1981, each terminal averaged over 55 hours of operation per week. A very flexible attitude to working hours has been the rule. An agreement was reached with the staff that the equipment would be used for up to 70 hours per week. Although jig and tool draughtsmen and numerical control programmers spend most of their working day at the terminals the majority of drawing office staff alternate between their drawing board, desk and the CAD terminal to suit their work patterns. A rolling programme, up-dated weekly, is administered by the supervisor of each system. This works well but needs experience to operate with the degree of flexibility necessary to cope with hourly changes in terminal requirements.

Productivity has grown steadily and reached about 3:1 overall. The learning curve took rather longer than originally planned because of the introduction of three systems within eighteen months and the heavy training load. The CAD supervisors contribute to the improvement of performance by acting as 'team-coaches'. They are directly involved in productive work and can advise on improved methods and ensure that every operator is kept up-to-date with developing techniques.

The organisation and development of the CAD/CAM facility is the responsibility of the CAE manager who was the secretary of the CAD working party and continues to have a co-ordinating role. Regular meetings are held with technical managers, their product engineering design groups, the CAD supervisors and all those using the system at frequent intervals. The CAD working party continues its steering role as part of the agenda of the Technical Managers' meeting. This assures continuity of the development of CAD/CAM strategy through the business. For the first time expensive capital equipment is installed in the design office and has to be managed accordingly to ensure a satisfactory return on the investment.

The main thrust of CAD/CAM is aimed at new product design since this is where most of the new drawings are generated. This approach ensures that the maximum benefit of CAM can be achieved. Also, since CAD is used at the beginning of the life cycle of each machine design, this is the fastest route to obtaining a full CAD/CAM data-base. The intention is to produce the final design layout of every machine on CAD thus capturing the geometry early and accurately. Then all subsequent requirements for this information can be met by access to the CAD data-base rather than by interpretation of conventional paperwork. The flow of CAD information from the design engineer is as shown opposite.

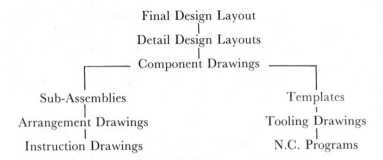

Final Design Layout

Detail Design Layouts

Component Drawings

Sub-Assemblies

Arrangement Drawings

Instruction Drawings

Templates

Tooling Drawings

N.C. Programs

CAD has also been used to advantage for the production of drawings required for process plant installations. Standard outlines of the constituent machines are made on CAD and can be manipulated to form the sales layout (proposal) drawing for the plant. Since there is usually a sequence of these drawings, worthwhile savings can be made through to final erection and foundation drawings:

Preliminary Strip Layouts

Final Sales Layout

Plant Arrangement Drawings

Foundation Plans

Erection Drawings

Service Drawings

It can be seen that the main benefits of CAD are achieved through repetitive sequences of work: similar shapes and repeated text on an individual drawing, a family of similar drawings or the sequence of drawing information from design to manufacture and from first sales proposal drawing to final installation drawings. In most cases it is found that CAD does not make much impact on the direct productivity of individual drawings starting from scratch.

There are considerable advantages to the designer at the conceptual stage where there is a need to piece together accurate geometry and to try out various alternative relationships of equipment and mechanisms.

We find that a balance has to be drawn to achieve the best advantages of a combination of traditional manual skills, including sketching and model-making, and the accuracy and stability of geometry produced on CAD. It can be a mistake for the designer to start with CAD too early in the design stage. Freedom of thought can be inhibited by leaning too heavily on the information which is already in the CAD data-base. It is necessary to understand that a CAD/CAM system is no more than a willing slave in order to reap the benefits of computer aided technology.

CAD is least effective where it is necessary to load the system with a large amount of existing manual drawing data before constructive work can begin. This should always be kept to a minimum. For example, do not load complete sets of standards but add to the data-base when the need arises. However, a certain amount will always be needed. Loading this information has to be taken as part of the learning curve and may be discounted over the useful life of the design because of the likely frequency of recall for design up-dates and modifications.

Perhaps a word should be said about the environment in the design office. The CAD terminals are grouped within the draughting area but screened by curtains to avoid unwanted reflections caused by the main office lighting and by low angle sunlight. It has therefore been necessary to provide additional adjustable lighting adjacent to the screens for reference to drawings and other information. The computers, disc drives and plotters are housed behind glass screen partitions. This means that the noise of the equipment does not cause distraction yet everyone can see what is happening. The computer rooms are separately air-conditioned and kept under temperature and humidity control 24 hours each day. This may well be a contributory factor to the high reliability of the hardware and the comparatively small amount of difficulty with ink-flow and paper on the plotters.

It was decided at the outset that all the graphics screens would be grouped adjacent to the CAD computer. This helped considerably to build confidence during the early stages. Now that all the staff are fully-trained and understand the technicalities of CAD/CAM operations it may be appropriate to consider remote location around the office of some of the screens. This can be an advantage where, for example, a designer is a member of a small team and finds it difficult to be away from his normal place of work because of the frequency of queries. This has to be reconciled with the distinct advantage which has been demonstrated of having designers, draughtsmen and production engineering staff working in close proximity, sharing the same graphics screens and the same data-base.

When CAD was first introduced it was decided that, since established manual drawing office procedures — which were quite efficient — and CAD work would have to co-exist for some years, it would be advisable, initially, to operate with a minimum of change to the existing methods. This has enabled staff to translate to computer graphics without the chore of having to learn new disciplines for numbering and registering drawings and the like. With CAD/CAM know-how well established in the office it is possible to predict what improvements need to be made to operating procedures. Aids must be developed, too, for improved management of the increasing amount of data which is being accumulated in various forms such as drawing files, patterns, standards, numerical control programs and security back-ups. It is clear that a computer-based archiving system will eventually be necessary. This may well be coupled with computer output on microfilm and the provision of microfilm viewing facilities adjacent to the designer or, possibly, the use of video-disc technology.

A few examples of our experiences with the application of CAD/CAM serve to illustrate the wide range of benefits to be obtained. The use of the parametric programming facility has enabled complex sets of side frames for printing presses to be issued from the drawing office in a few weeks whereas manual re-drawing work used to take several months. This not only shows direct productivity but also reduces the delivery cycle of the press by three months as well as allowing the time saved to be used on new design work. Using CAD techniques enabled the drawings for a new dough mixer to be issued very quickly for manufacture. This was very important in itself because of the tight delivery promise. The other advantage was gained at assembly, where every part of the first machine fitted together without difficulty. Thus the unplanned work on assembly was less than one half per cent of the cost of the machine. Also the assembly was completed within the time allowed thus helping to achieve the required delivery.

Traditionally the manufacture of biscuit-cutting rolls has involved a high level of manual skill. Firstly, in the design of the biscuit shape, then in constructing an accurate template and finally, hand-finishing of the engraved roll with about 150 impressions on each roll. With the introduction of CAD it was realised that the geometry of even quite complicated biscuit designs could be drawn quickly on the graphics screen. This would enable N.C. programs to be made very quickly since most of the work involves creating statements of the geometry. Thus a Bostomatic computerized numerical control machine tool was justified. The combination of CAD for the biscuit design and CAM for the numerical control program has resulted in a cycle time reduction from four months to three weeks. The finished roll is more consistently accurate than those produced by other methods. These advantages have greatly increased our share of the biscuit cutting roll market and produced a very satisfactory return on the investment.

Now that CAD/CAM is firmly established in the company many more opportunities for the exploitation of these techniques are being found. CAD/CAM has been one of several computer aids which has brought the designer and the production engineer very much closer together, organisationally and physically, to apply their joint talent to the challenge of economic manufacture.

It has always been clear that the creative role of the designer is paramount for successful product design. For higher quality design, more accurately and productively executed, for strong links between the designer and the production engineer, for economic and consistent manufacture to tight delivery schedules, for the provision of fast access to engineering data and for management control, it is equally clear that the powerful tools now being provided by information technology are an essential part of the design environment.

4

An Application of Information Technology in Manufacturing

DANIEL WARD

Motor Industry Correspondent of The Engineer Magazine

A MODERN car manufacturing plant involves some 10,000 workers putting together more than a million components to produce 1000 cars daily to a vast array of different specifications. The opportunity for chaos is considerable as a shortage of one critical component will bring the whole plant to a standstill, in the same way as a machine breakdown or undetected absenteeism in one department could. If a machine fault goes unnoticed and the poor quality parts it makes go unchecked, the quality of the car will suffer. Even ensuring that the customer in Reading gets the white model with red interior, a sunroof, mudflaps and spotlights he ordered, is a highly complex task.

The demand for a highly sophisticated information system in a factory is undeniable. If production managers are to run the plant efficiently, producing as many cars as possible and to the highest quality standard, they must be able to 'see' what is happening on the shopfloor constantly. This 'seeing' is provided by information technology in the form of detailed production and quality data which is rapidly updated for accuracy.

A correct decision can only be taken when all the relevant information is available at their fingertips. When both car plants and the cars themselves were crude and simple, production scheduling was easy because there were few model variants, checking quality was left to the domineering foreman, and no-one bothered if a number of unfinished cars had to stand on one side of the production line until the missing components arrived.

A car plant, like any manufacturing operation, is a series of linked processes. An operating decision in one department to, say, build all deluxe models for a week will create havoc unless it is communicated to all the other departments affected by the decision. It is no good painting a run of models navy blue, only to find the matching interior trim has yet to be made.

The high production rates of modern car plants demand that information is provided rapidly to ensure that the operation is kept running as near as possible to its peak efficiency. A delay in reacting to a hold-up means cars lost at the end of the day. The switch from labour intensive car making to today's philosophy of using fewer workers in a highly automated plant, means the cost of having the factory standing idle while a hitch is sorted out is enormous.

Information technology has revolutionised the efficiency of car making. Gone are the days when the bare minimum of information was collated manually on charts for daily or weekly assessment. Electrical monitoring systems of the last decade were a step in the right direction but they merely alerted the supervisor to major production problems — he still had to go to the other side of the plant to look at it before making a decision.

The tumbling price of the microchip means it is economic to monitor vastly more information from every corner of the plant than was conceivable before. It has long been physically possible to closely monitor the operating conditions of each machine but the obstacle of wiring up the maze of these circuits made it totally unviable. Now a silicon chip contains thousands of these circuits on its surface.

Not only does information technology provide precise data from every step in the long process of making a car, but the information is transmitted rapidly across the entire factory and even to small plants making components some distance away. After years of concentration on designing more productive machines to actually make and assemble parts, production engineers have realised that efficient data processing is the key to making a complex manufacturing plant efficient and profitable. At its simplest level this involves communicating as rapidly as possible that a machine has stopped so that production can be quickly restored. It is a considerable advance to be able to accurately identify which machine or conveyor is the culprit.

British Leyland's Mini Metro plant at Longbridge on the outskirts of Birmingham, stands as a ready showcase of information technology's vital role in making car manufacturing efficient in terms of both low cost of production and consistent high quality. This state-of-the-art factory cost £250 million when it produced the first trend setting Metro in 1980.

A simple measure of the effectiveness of Longbridge's sophisticated control and monitoring systems is the ability to consistently produce the number of cars scheduled each day. On the face of it this seems to be an insignificant achievement but from the old plant with its labour intensive and largely manual monitoring systems the production manager was doing well to make 70 per cent of the cars he had planned for at the beginning of the day.

Simple machine breakdowns, delays in repairing them, bottlenecks in various production departments or shortages of parts, all contributed to this 'more luck than judgement' method of production. Today the Longbridge managers boast of reaching 98 per cent of their production target regularly and it has hit an unprecedented 100 per cent on some days. With the massive investment in machinery this is the only way to make a profit and get good quality. The much revered Japanese car industry attains more than 95 per cent of planned production.

Changes in the paint shop highlight the advances that have been made. In a conventional spray booth where most of the painting was done by an army of men equipped with spray guns, only about half the finished painted bodyshells were of an acceptable quality. The rest had to be returned for drips and runs to be eliminated, a costly and time consuming process. With the help of computer controlled spraying arms and a sophisticated monitoring system continually checking operating conditions, such as optimum temperature, paint viscosity, etc., up to 90 per cent of the bodies are painted satisfactorily first time, requiring no rectification. Few plants have reached this level of efficiency but the cost saving is huge.

A crucial part of information technology for a manufacturing plant, is not just being able to make decisions with the aid of up to the minute dynamically generated data, but the flexibility it brings.

When selling his T model in the early days of the motor car, Henry Ford told customers they could have any colour as long as it was black. Today's choice of a dozen colours on mass produced cars would have been unworkable then because the plant could only cope with one model in one colour, as this kept production scheduling and component supply at their simplest level. Even as late as the 1950s most mass produced cars were black, special models had to be prepared very expensively 'off line'. Not even Rolls-Royce has been able to withstand the move to the modern style of production.

The car industry like many others has undergone a significant change but it is unimaginable that it could have done it without information technology. In its continual attack on product cost, the industry has switched from meeting the wide ranging demands of the customer by producing a large number of different models from an array of relatively small factories. The steeply rising cost of this method of satisfying the consumer was doomed for extinction in the 1970s and 1980s.

Longbridge provides a good example of the trend for the future which has been dictated by the high cost of automated machinery to build the bodyshell and engines of today's cars. Information technology provides the flexibility within a single car plant to produce a spread of models all based on the same basic bodyshell and just two basic engines. Metro can meet the demands for simple and basic transport or high performance small car luxury from one plant while still exploiting the economies of volume production. In case this sounds like the answer to all car machinery problems, it must be emphasised that the production scheduling of the vast number of derivatives is a mammoth job. Added to this is the implication of the shift towards fitting all of a car's optional extras — spotlights, mudflaps and rear wash/wipe — not at the dealer as before but on the production line. Although this is cheaper it once again makes scheduling a task which could not be managed manually.

Before explaining the role of information technology in a plant like Longbridge it is worth outlining the processes involved in building a modern car.

Production starts with coils of sheet steel being pressed into the desired shape to form doors, bonnets, boot panels and roofs, etc. Apart from these familiar panels the body structure is made up of numerous small brackets and pressings. The pressed panels are ferried to the body building area where the bare unpainted shell called a body-in-white is welded together. The next step is to clean and then paint the bodyshell before despatching it down the final assembly lines.

Here the windows are put in along with electrical wiring, lights, interior trim and finally the finished body gets an engine and gearbox, wheels and suspension. Lastly the car is checked to ensure that everything works before leaving the plant for delivery to a dealer.

Like all manufacturing plants, Longbridge aims to match production precisely to sales and information technology allows this to be done much more accurately than ever before. The old system of producing cars with what was thought to be the right mix of colours and specifications and then hunting around for customers, could not be tolerated any more because of its costly inefficiency.

BL stores all customer sales orders on a large mainframe computer at its Redditch data centre — one of the most powerful computer centres in Europe. When the production control department at Longbridge wants to plan the mix of Metro models for the forthcoming three weeks its minicomputer searches through the order bank for the 5000 highest priority orders.

Communication between Redditch and the plant is achieved by BL's own microwave network. It handles computer data, viewdata, electronic messages and up to 15,000 telephone calls an hour. From here it is possible to communicate with all BL's component plants spread across the country which will have to respond to the exact model and specification mix of the sales orders.

Details of Metro orders are stored on the minicomputer's disc pack, consisting of a floppy disc, rotating like a record on a turntable, with a rim speed of 150 mile/hour. Millions of characters of data stored on its magnetic surface can be recovered in a few thousandths of a second.

Once a work programme has been decided upon after reviewing the sales order bank, it is fed into the computer which communicates with all other departments. The purchasing department therefore has two and a half weeks' notice that, for instance, a Swedish specification Metro requiring a heavy duty rear wash/wipe kit will be built on a specific date. A computer control system will prevent that body starting its journey down the final assembly line unless all the correct parts are available. Previously a shortage may have only been discovered when the cars appeared on the final assembly track at the work station where the part is normally fitted. The only solution would have been to store the partly finished cars until more Swedish wash/wipe kits arrived from the component maker several days later.

Why this highly complex information system involves micro computers sending data upwards to a minicomputer which then pushes it on to the central mainframe, is because it is the most flexible and economic method. Minis and micros provide a much cheaper route which will become even more cost effective in the future as the number of circuits squeezed on to silicon chips continues to increase.

The flexibility comes from processing as much data as possible locally on the shopfloor, only communicating a small portion of the total information needed for overall control to a higher level. Longbridge's communications are handled by four and a half miles of special co-axial cabling called Videodata. It links over 200 terminals — normally combined keyboard and visual display screens where information is keyed in by an operator and received on the screen —plus 24 computers and over 100 computer monitoring and control systems.

With the manufacturing work programme set for the day, the cars begin to take shape. Arrival of body panels in metal cages — pallets — from the Swindon pressing plant is pre-notified via the microwave communications network. Incoming supplies to the Longbridge store are checked by a man running a light pen across a bar code on the pallet identification ticket. Details of the type of panels and the number and arrival time are then automatically stored in the management system's minicomputer.

Light pens are widely used in the Metro plant. They have taken over from an operator manually transcribing details from one card or form to another. As the old system was always prone to human error, a modern day solution was required. The bar code is a series of varying thickness black lines. As the light pen is moved laterally across the strip the computer interprets the resulting electrical pulses as a unique code without any chance of error. It is also much faster. BL has used bar codes to identify cars and components in the same way that supermarkets have adopted the system for food.

The body assembly process effectively starts with the automated panel store. The store is a 45 foot high racking system covering the area of a football pitch which stores body panels in pallets. The computer not only controls where the driverless cranes place each pallet in the store but remembers exactly what is in the pallet. The computer management system also eliminates traffic jams among the cranes by distributing panels evenly throughout the store. Only four cranes are needed where eight were needed before, largely because the computer plans each entry of a new pallet and withdrawal for supply to the production line. In this way pallets are picked up and dropped off at more or less the same point in the store.

The overall performance of the store is very impressive, moving pallets at the rate of one in and one out every 57 seconds yet no more than five people run the whole system. The old procedure of writing instructions down on paper and manually processing reams of data, could never approach the speed and efficiency of the new computer controlled store.

The old Longbridge store was typical of many factory stock systems. A written advice note accompanied incoming goods but only in a small proportion of cases was it possible to take the trouble to check that the pallet really did contain what the note indicated.

The pallet was then placed on the floor in the vast open stores. However, because its location was only roughly specified by aisle number, consignments often went missing, leaving the poor fork-lift truck driver to go and look for it among the mass of panels.

Having little confidence in the manually processed data inevitably meant managers over compensated by increasing the number of panels held in the store. Considerable faith in the new computer system means the old costly inventories have been dramatically reduced. If there is any doubt about exactly what is held in the store, the computer can be interrogated by the operator until the required information is presented.

The panels are delivered to the production lines where they are welded together to form large assemblies such as the entire floor section and complete body sides. The next step is to weld all the major parts together to produce something which resembles a Metro for the first time.

Like all modern car plants much of the body welding on the Metro line is done by robots. There is nothing magical about their capabilities. The robot is taught to perform a certain task by an operator. The precise movements are stored in an electronic memory. It is to this that the robot's microprocessor goes each time the welding cycle is to be performed for detailed instructions on where to move and when to weld.

The robot is a considerable aid to quality as it puts the welds in the same precise position day after day and never misses one. If it stops welding for any reason the monitoring system informs the line supervisor immediately which welds have been missed. Robots are also used for the messy job of spraying underseal on to the bottom of the Metro bodyshell, applying adhesive to interior trim panels and handling bulky panels.

More sophisticated robots are already being developed, capable of picking up randomly placed objects. Up to now this has perhaps been the ultimate test for a robot because it cannot 'think' for itself. But the use of a camera which feeds back information to the robot's micro-computer allows it to interpret the images and direct the robot hand accurately to pick up the object. Renault and Fiat have led the way in the research into what is now called the second generation of robots capable of doing many more of the boring or arduous jobs in car factories.

From the robot welding lines the bodies go upstairs to the vast overhead body-in-white store in readiness for the half a mile conveyor journey to the paint shop. The store is like a massive car park for wheelless bodies, providing space for 140 bodies in ten storage lanes. Movement of the bodies into the stores, lane selection and transfer to the exit lifts is all handled by three programmable logic controllers —PLCs.

These PLCs contain a mass of solid state circuitry on silicon chips and by virtue of their comparatively low cost it is possible to monitor a vast number of mechanical functions. The chief operating difference between a PLC and a minicomputer is that the PLC is not re-programmable, it is designed to perform certain operations and cannot be adapted to do others.

The bodies move on motorised trolleys — platens, each of which is uniquely identified by a system of coded lugs. As a body enters the store an automatic reading device updates the store control system with the details of the newly arrived bodyshell. The person controlling the store is provided with operating information on a display screen and a computer generated store lane map which is dynamically updated whenever a body arrives or leaves the store. When a batch selection has been made of bodies to be painted the same colour, the computer management system tells the PLCs which platen to move from which lane and where they are going.

Emphasising that a purely manual control system cannot provide the sophisticated decision making of the Metro set-up, the body store has to despatch a shell to the paint shop every 29 seconds. Failure by human operators to decide which body to send in that time scale would result in a gap in the line of bodies in the paint shop, and so lost production.

The role of the three PLCs is to provide the three lines in the paint shop with the required specification of bodies to satisfy the sales orders. The PLCs therefore have to communicate with the paint shop control system which runs on the main plant mini computer. This computer management system aids production flow through the paint plant by batching bodies to be painted the same colour together and ensuring that if the desired colour is temporarily not available the body requiring that colour remains in the store. Previously the body would have gone into the paint shop before the hitch was discovered.

The information from the paint shop operators will keep the body-in-white store informed of paint shortages or other production problems. The ability to carefully batch bodies according to colour is vital to the efficiency of the paint shop.

Information technology reduces the need for cleaning out the spray guns which saves paint and thinners. The quality of the paint improves and there is less wear and tear on the equipment. This saves money.

Before the bodies get their first lick of paint a computer controlled labelling device attaches a metal tag denoting colour and batch number to each body. At the manual first station in the paint shop the operator knows what colour to use.

BL's computer technology subsidiary, BL Systems, is justifiably proud of the complex information technology it developed for the Metro plant, but probably the most advanced single system and not surprisingly the hardest to perfect was the painted body store set up.

At the lowest level the engineers could have been satisfied with computerising the old manual system of simply ensuring that the painted bodies got the right trim fitted on the final assembly line and the appropriate engine and gearbox. This had been achieved in the old works by some forty men — bodyhandlers — darting round the incoming bodies checking individual index cards to achieve a rough and ready scheduling on to the final assembly line. The store had a capacity of only twenty bodies so bottlenecks and delays soon brought the preceding departments to a standstill.

Even a straightforward computerised control system would not have overcome the established problem of having too many workers on the final assembly tracks — a high labour area of car plants which cannot be as easily automated as painting or body manufacture.

The time it takes to install the luxury wood door cappings and numerous other features to a top of the range Vanden Plas Metro is clearly much longer than for the more spartan specification of the low cost Metro City. To cope with the occasions when a series of luxury models go down the final assembly tracks together, car makers have traditionally employed enough men on the line to ensure all the work is completed in the specified cycle time.

The cost burden of this system is evident when a series of basic models is built — there are substantially more men than required. The answer to eliminating this inherent over-manning is to have a sophisticated vehicle sequencing system which ensures that the work content of each of the three lines is always balanced, thereby preventing the problems of building several models of one type at the same time on one track. The workforce was immediately reduced by 115 in the final assembly area when the computerised system was installed in Longbridge.

Taking only body type, paint colour and engine derivative the computer has to consider 9240 possible combinations of Metro. It cannot ignore the maximum feasible number of variants which is a mind boggling figure approaching infinity. Emphasising the enormity of the computer system's task is the speed at which it must operate. A decision of what type of model is to be built and on which line, is taken every 42.8 seconds, for 16 hours a day, but the computer is allowed only seven seconds to make its mind up.

In order to develop all the rules governing the computer's sequencing decisions, BL Systems developed an ingenious computer simulation technique called SEE WHY. Imagine it as a computer system which once fed with the rules of chess will play the game on a colour graphics screen according to instructions but will never break the rules or cheat. The most important feature of SEE WHY is that you can change the rules and then see what effect it has on the game just by watching the screen.

Working with basic operating parameters of production rates and the number of final assembly tracks and rules like: do not send two luxury models down the same track consecutively or put Vanden Plas interior trim into a Metro intended to be a police panda car, SEE WHY sorts out the logistics nightmare. It was by using this simulation technique that the optimum capacity of the painted body store was determined. Because of its ability to simulate factory layouts and production flow and thereby eliminate bottlenecks and optimise complex organisational problems, SEE WHY has been used outside the automotive field by the Post Office and British Airways.

BL Systems' Longbridge vehicle sequencing system continually collects data from both the trim and assembly tracks and the painted body store. Armed with this information it goes through a decision making routine: Is the trim track calling for the next painted body?; what kind of model can that particular track handle subject to current work content and material constraints? — a check is then carried out to see whether the derivative most out of balance with the plant's weekly production target can be launched without violating the production rules held by the computer; is there a painted body in the store matching the requested type and if so what colour is it? If there is more than one body meeting the requirement the oldest will be selected; is there a sales order submitted and selected for this model type and colour? Again the highest priority one is selected; what is its full specification? Is its work content appropriate for the chosen track? Is there a crane available to collect the body?

In the seven seconds available to the computer to make a decision it does not go through the above process once but indeed as many times as necessary until a perfect match is achieved, thereby selecting the best choice of model at that moment to go down the assembly tracks.

The painted body store itself is controlled by one computer and five minicomputers. The crane control needed for delivering and fetching bodies resembles that used in the panel autostore at the beginning of the production process. There is also a dynamically updated store map giving each body location like that in the body-in-white store. Highlighting the huge impact of information technology, the forty former body handlers have been replaced by just four technicians operating the keyboard control stations.

Another facet of the vehicle sequencing system involves reacting to component stock control information. When stocks have fallen below a specified minimum level the sequencing system is notified that, for instance, only 50 more Italian specification headlamps are available. Only 50 Metros bound for Italy will be sent down the line unless an instruction is received that the shortage has been overcome.

Once again the information technology systems play a vital role in preventing the production system from being fouled up by cars that cannot be passed down the flow line because of a fault or component shortage.

The assembly lines are also provided with information via computer terminals on what components will be needed and on which track, in order to meet the specifications of the various derivatives. So the line broadcasting alerts the trim, instrument, tyre and engine stores of the arrival of a certain model on one of the three tracks.

Previously, there was a huge and costly stock inventory because every conceivable component was stored by the line irrespective of whether the model requiring those parts was being built that day or not.

If all this information technology appears to be fool-proof it is worth mentioning that there is still room — diminished though it is — for human error. Until the stock control is fully computerised down to the last nut and bolt, component makers wrongly labelling boxes of parts will remain a cause of frustration. Even in the most sophisticated car plant a shortage of critical parts used on all models such as wheels, will inevitably halt production irrespective of how many computers control the factory.

Although highly sophisticated control and monitoring systems have played their important part in bringing the Metro to the final assembly line, the role of information technology is still a vital tool for management in the last stages of the manufacturing process. As the bodies move down the trim and assembly tracks a vehicle tracking system monitors their progress until they are accepted by sales department at the end of the line. Management can quickly check how many cars of which type are nearing completion.

Once completed each Metro passes an engine and brake test on rotating rollers before being subjected to a computer controlled electrical systems check. This is a good example of how low cost computerisation has enabled the quality of the product to be improved by checking many more components and systems for faults than was previously possible.

Before, if the lights and wipers worked properly no one bothered very much. Now the inspector sits in the car and the computer instructs him to go through detailed checks of every electrical function. Commands and questions appearing on an adjacent display screen to ensure nothing is missed. Not only is a read-out of the performance of each item obtained, but the computer processes the results over a period to assess whether there is a quality problem with one or two parts. It would be a time consuming job for a manager to plough through all the data in the hope of spotting quality trends.

From this point the car is taken over by sales. In the days when the Austin 1100 was produced at Longbridge, in the 1960s and before, the process of matching cars to orders was an athletic and error prone exercise. A gang of men would stand at the head of the line until a model of a certain colour was spotted. A rummage through a huge rack of pigeon holes containing sales orders hopefully yielded the appropriate piece of paper. The chassis and engine number then had to be manually transposed on to various check sheets. A haphazard system indeed. With the finished models boasting many more detailed extras the chances of manually matching the car to an extensive sales order are unacceptably low.

BL Systems has replaced the old paper system with its computerised Minivics set-up. Comparing vehicle data generated by the line tracking system with sales orders held by the main Longbridge computer, the Minivics rapidly matches finished Metros to specific orders. Automatically prepared 'release papers' including vehicle details, the BL distributor's name and address and the delivery instructions, are placed with each car.

Continuing the use of the all important identification bar code even the factory police on the exit gates prevent a lorry load of Metros going astray by running a light pen across each vehicle's documents.

As has been shown, information technology plays a vital role in working alongside people and automated machinery to make a factory highly productive and efficient. And it is no less important when there is a fault and the production line has ground to a halt.

Lost production or building unfinished cars because some components are missing are the chief crimes in a vehicle factory. But as all production plants break down sometime — there are no exceptions as the totally reliable factory has yet to be built — the task for information technology is to get it back into action as fast as possible.

Slow and often inefficient maintenance of machines is the bugbear of most plants but the previous communications systems hardly helped matters. Maintenance sheds dotted around the works were each provided with a mimic screen — a diagrammatic display of the adjacent production line and associated machines.

When something stopped, a light would flash on the board to provide a rough location of the fault. But because the sysem was not sophisticated enough to identify the type of problem the electrician inevitably left the shed to discover after a five minute walk to the machine, that it was a mechanical fault and vice versa. Every moment wasted meant more cars lost.

Some would say this was not a bad system as it replaced the procedure whereby the foreman on a particular section of the line would telephone to say there was a fault only to find the maintenance staff out repairing a machine some distance away.

The Metro plant, and several others since, is equipped with a computer based system which communicates via numerical displays visible throughout the factory. The code displayed tells both line supervisors and maintenance staff exactly where a fault has occurred and the nature of the problem — simply whether the electrician or mechanical fitter should tend to the machine.

Because the PLCs — described earlier — can monitor a vast amount of data on the condition of each piece of plant, the local line manager can interrogate the computer from a keyboard terminal on the shopfloor and receive more information about the nature of the fault. BL Systems has installed a similarly sophisticated diagnostic system in the new Land Rover engine plant at Solihull.

The impact of information technology on the plant manager's job has been to allow him to concentrate on the real job in hand. The aim must be to continually improve the efficiency and cost effectiveness of the factory while at the same time planning and solving problems with long term solutions. Once again Longbridge is a good example of what can be achieved. Today's approach has replaced the old philosophy of simply trying to keep the line moving.

Previously the BL plant manager received the manually processed data on production rates, number of cars lost, how many unfinished cars there were, etc., at the end of each eight hour shift. If there had been a problem it was invariably too late to do anything about it and anyway the men had just gone home to be replaced by the next shift, so the problem went unchecked for a day or more.

The Metro production controller receives this information every hour at no more than three minutes past the hour thanks to the computer monitoring. Any problem can be speedily tackled. If the data arrived instead at ten minutes past the hour it would already be out of date and of minimal immediate use.

Once a production or quality problem has been spotted the controller can quickly interrogate the computer for more information. For instance, because the exact location and specification of each car being built is known — from continual checking of the bar coded identification — it can soon be determined whether a problem has arisen in one department because of that day's specific model mix.

There appears to be nothing outside the scope of information technology. Even the traditional clocking-on system of men punching individual cards in a wall mounted clock has been computerised. Now controlled by micro processor, the data recorded on each card can be processed centrally, cutting by one third the time it takes to prepare the weekly payroll. Also management can rapidly determine how many men are present in each area and balance manning according to that day's scheduled production.

To make a modern man-produced car to high quality standards

demands constant monitoring at all stages of production. In the early days of the motor car no-one ever thought of checking its shape to see how straight and true it had been made. If the fit of certain panels or the doors was not good enough they were carefully reworked by hand with a hammer and file. All this costs money, much better to aim to make each body to high dimensional accuracy so every door and bootlid fits properly first time. This production engineer's utopia has now been achieved.

Not surprisingly it is impossible to measure the complex shape of a car with a tape measure. Although measuring machines have been available for many years their manual operation meant it took days to completely check one body, by which time if there was a problem, hundreds of cars had already gone through in a similar condition.

The advent of a computer controlled three dimensional measuring machine has reduced the measuring time to no more than four hours for the extremely detailed checking. The computer tells the measuring probe where to position itself and then records the dimension which is automatically compared with the correct standard measurement stored in its memory. At the end of the cycle the operator receives a complete print out of the dimensions which are outside the permitted tolerance. From this the fault can be traced back to either the way the panels were pressed or damage incurred during assembly.

Although the total information technology systems at the Metro plant are highly advanced and probably some of the most sophisticated used by car makers today, inevitably the engineers would like even more control over the complex manufacturing processes. Ever mindful that a new Metro is scheduled to be produced each minute they would like a greater level of integration of the systems controlling each department so reducing the time it takes to react to a hiccup.

For instance, it is easy to see the advantage of being able to instantly communicate with all affected departments that the blue paint in the paint shop has dirt in it and cannot be used. The sooner the trim shop stops making the matching blue seats and switches to the next colour selected by the paintshop, the lower the stock inventory will be.

All car makers are attacking the size of their stock inventories, right from coils of steel waiting to be made into body panels to boxes of light bulbs. It is hugely expensive to have components hanging around inside the plant for weeks before actually using them in a car. However only with a considerable investment in information technology as seen at Longbridge can the production line be operated smoothly on very low stocks without continually falling foul of component shortages.

Despite the fundamental role of information technology in modern factories the robot is more often than not given credit in the layman's mind with efficiency and the latest technology. This is particularly the case with the Fiat Strada where shuffling body shells featured in a distinctive television commercial. No one could be in any doubt that the Fiat was indeed 'built by robot'.

It was the overall computerised control network rather than the conventional microprocessor operated robots which was the success of this imaginative system. Fiat decided not to weld the Strada bodies on a conventional long conveyor line with robots each side, but to design a more flexible set-up. It is the information systems which prove this flexibility.

The body panels are hung together as a loose bodyshell on a driverless computer controlled trolley. While the trolley follows a transmitting cable sunk in the floor, the computer dictates which way it turns on the journey to the robot welding stations. The trolley is commanded to wait and subsequently enter a robot station where five or six robots apply spot welds according to the relayed information on its model type.

The system is specifically designed to have the flexibility to make several different models according to what the sales department requires. The management control system will instruct each of the numerous trolleys to receive welds at the required number of robot stations — the robots at each station applying welds to a different part of the body.

Should the robots at one station break down, the central computer will reorganise the movements of the trolleys to compensate. Also the remaining robots can be instructed to add the welds missed out.

Fiat has used the same philosophy to build an advance engine assembly plant of the future. It shares some of the thinking behind the Metro vehicle sequencing system.

The specifications of engines, like cars, vary considerably despite being based on the same major components for a certain model. Like

BL Systems' planners, Fiat engineers wanted to eliminate the wasteful principle of having surplus men on the engine assembly line in order to cope with the most complex specification.

Instead of having the speed of the line slow enough to build the most difficult engine it was decided to assemble the engines at separate work stations and largely dispense with a fixed line. Here each operator works at his own pace.

The engines are ferried to each work station and on to the next stage of assembly by smaller brothers of the pallets used to build the Fiat Strada. There are thirty seven of these battery powered trolleys. The overall computer management system is very similar to that developed previously for the robot welding concept.

Not only is the operator able to 'call' the computer for his next engine but in the tea breaks empty trolleys go to each work station and collect the used racks of nuts, bolts and parts needed for the engines. They are then programmed to return to the stores for more supplies so the operator is greeted with replenished parts boxes when he returns to his work station.

To achieve this sophisticated type of systems control manually, there would be more operators in the control room trying to establish order from the chaos than actual workers on the shopfloor screwing engines together.

Without information technology these imginative methods of raising efficiency in factories and improving working conditions by relieving workers of the more repetitive tasks could not be attempted. For the future, information technology is the only way!

5

An Application of Information Technology in Retailing

SIMON OREBI GANN

Systems Development Manager, Marks & Spencer P.L.C.,
London

IN ORDER to maximise his sales a retailer needs one very important commodity, information on those sales. He must know what lines sell (so that he can restock them rapidly), and what lines do not sell (so that he does not tie up further wasted capital by buying more of them). If he operates many shops he needs to know this information separately for each shop, as there may be a geographical variation of sales: if it rains in one part of the country the shops there are more likely to have sold umbrellas than those with fine weather, and accordingly will need to be restocked.

Goods do not normally count as sold until they have been paid for — a trite statement that is relevant because it makes it clear that the earliest time at which information can be sensibly collected about sales is at the Point of Sale itself, in other words at the till. Information on sales may in principle be gathered at any later time, for example by counting the remaining stock at the end of the month to deduce what has been sold, but as the need for more accurate and speedily available information grows, the emphasis moves to recording sales information as the customer sale is made.

A cheap and effective means of measuring sales, used sometimes in the case of high-priced merchandise sold in small numbers (such as furniture or cars), is to record the information manually on a piece of paper. This becomes increasingly inaccurate, ineffective and costly as the items get smaller (imagine for a moment a housewife who has bought a fortnight's supply of food for a large family in a supermarket having to wait while, as well as each item's price being rung on the till, a manual note of the item's description is taken).

In the 1950s some retailers found an equivalent but faster method of recording sales which became, and still is, quite popular especially for sales of more expensive clothing. The approach is to attach a small pre-printed cardboard tag to each item as part of the manufacturing process; the tag is then removed by the sales assistant as the sale is made. If, as well as being printed with the item's description, the tag is punched with a series of holes which can be read by a machine, it is only necessary for a shop's tags to be passed through such a machine for a full record of all its sales to be available. This system is reasonably cheap and requires relatively few machines to read the tags and summarise the information.

In many situations tags are a totally satisfactory solution and one particularly suitable for recording sales of mid-priced merchandise which sells in reasonable volume. They are likely to continue in use in some areas for the next decade.

There are, however, various disadvantages with the use of tags which make them unacceptable in many instances. There are, for example, many goods (such as food lines) where it is not practicable to attach tags. It should also be observed that most retailers buy their goods from a variety of suppliers, and it is only in cases where buying is in adequate bulk that a manufacturer is likely to be prepared to attach the particular type of tag used by a retailer to the goods which he has bought. It is not possible for manufacturers automatically to tag everything which they make because there is no single standard of tag in use and each retailer selects the type of tag which he wishes to adopt. Even in those circumstances when using a tag is feasible the corresponding sales information is not immediately available as there is a time delay in deriving it; the tags must first be read, and the pure handling and transport represents an overhead which may be unwanted both in terms of cost and timescale.

Attention has therefore moved to the till itself. One thing that all items sold have in common is that their prices are rung up on a till as part of the sales process; the question must be whether it is possible to use this process itself to capture the sales information. A conventional till simply acts as an adding machine together with the physical storage of money. (It is not unusual for a till drawer to need to hold half a hundredweight of change which poses considerable engineering design difficulties when it comes to arranging that a motor can open the drawer at all, and that if it does so the drawer does not open past the required point!) The only details recorded are the price of each item, sub-totals, totals and possibly the amount tendered by the customer and the change which should be given.

Over the last decade, tills have become more intelligent. Many modern tills allow items to be classified into convenient groups; a discount warehouse, for example, might choose to use groups for white goods (washing machines and refrigerators), hi-fi equipment, and portable radios. The shop staff can interrogate the till whenever convenient and it will give a running total for the day of the takings by product group. This is better than no information at all, but it still does not give sales information at the detailed level by line. To obtain that, a more intelligent till is required, which begins to resemble a VDU or a microcomputer in its capabilities.

Such tills are now available and they fall into two classes. The first is effectively a 'dumb' terminal: it is connected to a minicomputer somewhere in the shop which provides it with its apparent intelligence. The second type has its own intrinsic intelligence; it contains a microprocessor which makes it effectively a dedicated microcomputer. Such a till can either be totally selfstanding or may be connected in a network with other similar tills so that information may be passed between them. Future developments are likely to be in this second category primarily for reasons of resilience. In a large shop with many tills the failure of the minicomputer used in the former class would paralyse the operation, leaving the shop unable to take customers' money (not a satisfactory situation). In the latter case failure of a single till is a relatively unimportant occurrence.

The cost of an intelligent till (usually called an Electronic Point of Sale terminal — abbreviated EPOS) is currently about three times that of a conventional till, and it is therefore necessary for a retailer to gain considerable benefits from the use of them to warrant the extra investment required. It might seem superficially that the only factor to be considered in installing EPOS tills is the need for speedily available and accurate Point of Sale information; that this is not the case becomes apparent if an examination is made of all the business procedures which may go on at a till point. Such an examination will also help to illustrate the general way in which a retailer must approach solving a business problem in which he considers using information technology.

The first, and simplest, operation at a till point is the ringing up of a customer's purchases. In order to capture sales details by individual line, it is necessary for the sales assistant to communicate to the till somehow what item it is that is being sold. This may be done in two main ways: either the assistant has to key a product's identifying code into the till, or the product's code is printed on the item's packaging in a machine readable way (for example as a bar code) and is read by a wand attached to the till. The wand, called such because of its shape, consists of a light source and a detector which register the position of characters or vertical bars on the packaging of an item and sends a series of pulses to the till which are decoded to form the product's identifying code. Now it is important to an efficient retailer that the extra administrative load of using a different tilling system, such as EPOS, is as low as possible, and it is therefore preferable if the increase of work at the till is kept to the minimum. One way in which this can be done is to use the till's intelligence to avoid the need for the assistant to key in the item's price as well as its identifying code; the till uses the code to search its memory and supply the price which is then displayed for the customer and the assistant to see. If this approach is adopted the assistant need only key in the code instead of the price that would be keyed on a conventional till, which means that the overall operating time should not increase substantially — in other words the cost of staffing tillpoints should not increase as a result of using EPOS terminals.

Mention should be made here of the Article Numbering Association (ANA) which has set up an international standard for the allocation of codes. By following the standard, a manufacturer ensures that his products all have a code which is unique, and may thus be printed on the packaging. The code may then be used directly by a retailer, who is thereby saved the cost and the potential error involved in having to mark the items himself so that his tills may perform price lookup.

Price lookup, however, raises its own particular problems: there is the question of till memory capacity and the maintenance of the price and the other product information.

Consider firstly the memory capacity. In order that an EPOS till be practical and cost effective, it is not normal to include external mass storage such as floppy discs or hard disc units. It is therefore necessary for the till to have sufficient internal memory capacity available for it to hold price information and other details on each line which the customer is allowed to purchase at it. As a policy many large stores prohibit a customer paying for an item other than at the nearest till, but others wish to give a better service by allowing a series of purchases to be paid for at one go, in which case it is necessary that every till in the store should have the capacity to hold details on every product sold in the store. The majority of tills currently available commercially have a capacity of several thousand items. A large shop may require several tens of thousands of items in order that its whole catalogue may be accessible from one till. There is, however, no doubt that the memory capacity of tills will increase considerably over the next few years as the new generation of 256 Kb (which is equivalent to 32,000 characters) memory chips become readily available.

Passing on from the problems of memory capacity there is the question of maintenance of the information in the till. The data held on each item is likely to be an identifying code, a text description, a price and possibly a couple of other pieces of information such as tax (for example VAT) rate and department code. This data can, in principle, change from day to day as items are added to or deleted from a store's catalogue and as price changes occur. The labour involved in keeping that information up-to-date in a till which may hold several thousand items' details is considerable. As a consequence it is normal for all the tills in the shop which deal with the same group of products to be able to communicate with each other on a local network, so that the item details need only be updated on one till and may then be transmitted automatically to the other tills in the group. This at least avoids the need for multiple maintenance of product details but the basic updates will need to be done once.

In order that the information gathered by the tills can be transmitted to a company's Head Office, where the sales' details can be summarised and analysed, the tills in a store are connected together and are then joined to a national network with the tills in the company's other shops. This network can, of course, be used for two-way communications so it is therefore possible for the maintenance of item details to be carried out centrally and transmitted daily to each shop. This has the benefit that it reduces the update workload to the absolute minimum.

There are more operations than the simple ringing up of merchandise taking place at a till point and it is important to consider the impact on them of using EPOS tills. Many retailers give credit as well as taking payment in cash; the credit may be either on the retailer's own credit scheme or may use one of the widely available credit cards. An EPOS till can play a very useful role in this situation, decreasing the load on the sales assistant. When a customer wishes to draw on an account with the retailer's own credit scheme, the EPOS till can be used as part of the complete transaction to interrogate the shop's own computer system (which may be either in the shop or may be accessible via the network) to ensure that the card has not expired or been stolen and that the customer is not exceeding his credit limit. The system then debits the customer's account with the value of the sale directly. For a customer who offers one of the normal credit cards, an automatic request for authorisation can be made to the credit company's computer if it, too, is connected to the same network as the shop, and the shop can pass full details of the sale to the credit company, thus authorising the transaction and speeding up the process by which the shop is paid — a worthwhile benefit.

Many large shops allow merchandise to be exchanged (such as an item of clothing which is the wrong size) or allow a refund to be made if requested by a customer. Both these situations have to be catered for by an EPOS terminal: in each case an item has to be added to the store's stock record and an adjustment may have to be made to the internal record of the till contents if a refund is given. Furthermore, the system has to be flexible enough to allow the sales assistant to input a different price for an item from the one which the system may currently hold: this is necessary to handle the case where the price of an item changes between the time when it was originally bought and the time at which a refund is given, as it is important that the refund is given at the old and not the current price. This sort of process is a simple one to handle manually but is far more complicated when it has to be built into the computer program which runs an EPOS till.

What additional advantages might a retailer hope to gain from installing an EPOS system? Basically, he will see a benefit if he can use the intelligence of the till to replace tasks which might be previously carried out manually. One example would be the situation in which sales assistants are paid partially on commission; the intelligence of the machine can then be used to calculate automatically the amount due, thus saving considerable clerical effort. The till can also be used to encourage multiple purchases by, for example, offering a discount when a customer buys several items of one line — such a bulk discount scheme is extremely costly to administer manually.

Analysis of the till information may actually bring further benefits. It becomes possible to monitor closely the number of transactions done in the shop by time of day and to organise the shop's staffing accordingly, leading to potentially large savings in staff time which may then be employed in the most effective way. An EPOS system does not, of course, provide all the answers. Records of stock levels will still require occasional manual checking because the EPOS system only registers true sales, in other words what actually goes through the till point. Stolen or damaged merchandise causes a loss that must be recorded in the system, which therefore has to allow manual stock count corrections to be input.

The benefits mentioned so far can be considered to be quantifiable, but the use of EPOS can also give rise to intangible benefits. One of these is the improved service which can be given to customers by speeding up the flow of people past the till point. This can be achieved in some cases where customers buy large numbers of items such as in supermarkets. Each item has the printed product identity code on it (referred to earlier) and the items are then fed along a conveyer past a laser scanner which reads the bar codes and passes the information to the till. The net effect is to reduce the handling of the goods and to speed up the processing. The cost, however, is such as to preclude its use in shops where the average customer purchase consists of a relatively small number of items.

In summary, the sort of benefits which a retailer would look for in using a Point of Sale system are:

rapidly available sales information; more accurate and consistent pricing; reduced clerical workload; improved stock control; improved staffing levels; simplified credit control; improved cash flow from credit companies; automatic calculation of sales assistants' commissions; improved service to the customer.

The sort of areas which may present difficulty and therefore must be examined in detail are:

maintenance of products' details in the system; handling of returns and exchanges; memory capacity of the till compared with the stores' catalogue size.

The use of EPOS systems is more advanced in the U.S.A. than in Europe, but the lesson, as with much in information technology, is that it is unwise to be the first user of any system!

Electronic Point of Sale has been used here as an illustration of the way in which the retailer must approach the application of information technology. There is no doubt that the next ten years will be an exciting time for all retailers and a time of great change. Computing power will become cheaper and more widely available and the tools available to the retailer will grow. There may also be a significant impact on the expectation of customers as a result of the increasing use of publicly available information technology services such as Viewdata (for example British Telecom's Prestel) and the imminent arrival of cable television. Both of these offer two-way communications and, in principle at least, will be available to the majority of the population. The domestic television will then become quite simply a computer terminal and will provide the user with a wide range of facilities. One of these is likely to be an extension of the existing shopping by mail order which will allow the customer to browse through the products offered by a series of retailers in the comfort of his armchair, and will then make it possible (and will probably encourage!) him to place an order directly.

As long as retailers do not forget that it is the customer who matters and not the technology, they will be able to control the tools that become available to them and will employ them in increasingly effective and profitable ways.

6

An Application of Information Technology in The Financial World

B J KEYTE

Senior Executive,
Planning & Development, Management Services Division,
National Westminster Bank PLC

MONEY, or more specifically monetary value, provides the prime information basic to any financial transaction. The names of the payer and beneficiary and the date of payment complete the essential information. In the case of cash transfers the transaction is completed by the exchange of notes ("I promise to pay, etc.") or coins which indicate the value involved. So much is written today about the automation of financial transactions that it is easy to forget that the vast majority (in volume if not in value) continue to take place through the exchange of cash. Undoubtedly, this remains a very convenient medium which even today, in terms of total acceptability, is hardly matched by other more automated means.

However, the high cost of handling cash, its issue, the continual replacement of paper notes and the security provisions which need to surround its movement and custody are often under-estimated. Whilst therefore 'the cashless society' which a number of enthusiastic bankers proclaimed was just around the corner as long ago as the mid-sixties may still be only on the far distant horizon, the movement of payment methods away from cash is still a desirable objective.

Information related to payments is the basis on which the largest financial systems are built; other more specialised functions have also been developed and together they form a range of applications, disciplines and techniques which in terms of automation are arguably more wide-spread and diverse than in any other industry. Certainly the growth of international banking with United Kingdom banks opening offices throughout the world and overseas banks well established in London, determines no shortage of competition in the offering of financial services. Nevertheless, whatever complex financial facilities may be required by the treasurers of multi-national conglomerates, the predominant interest of the man-in-the-street remains the need to have available a simple, cheap, reliable and secure payments system. It is this objective which has consequently attracted and continues to dominate the thinking of much of the finance industry.

The importance of cash in this regard has already been highlighted and the measure of the dependence on this medium can be assessed by considering the estimated total payments for 1980, by households, for the purchase of goods and services, as illustrated in Figure 1.

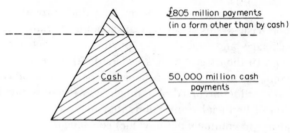

£805 million payments (in a form other than by cash)

Cash

50,000 million cash payments

Figure 1

It is perhaps noteworthy that payments by credit cards or through the automated services provided by the banks are even today so small compared with the total that they cannot be sensibly portrayed. However, together with cheque payments they form a significant volume and merit detailed consideration.

The cheque is a familiar payment document and with the spread of the banking habit to receive a cheque in payment for services or goods is a widely and totally accepted practice. The cheque card, which was introduced in 1966, has further contributed to the use of the cheque as a popular means of buying goods. Yet, essentially, the cheque remains a document conceived in a bygone age, and governed largely by an act of Parliament passed in the reign of Queen Victoria (Bills of Exchange

Act 1882). Will those who ponder new methods today develop systems which will still flourish 100 years from now? The cheque undoubtedly has proved a popular device and its use has grown steadily and currently shows little sign of abating as is illustrated in Figure 2.

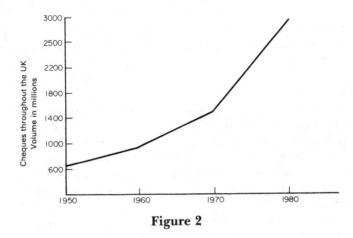

Figure 2

More recently credit cards have started to make an impact. Initially, and to some extent still, they were an American phenomenon. In the absence of a nationwide banking system and with an air transport system second to none, the United States traveller needed a means of payment when far from home. The credit card admirably met this need and in addition provided a ready means of payment and credit for local purchases when the business trips were over. In days of international travel the attractions have been readily appreciated and taken up all over the world. The systems developed have, however, been largely manual with multi-part forms being completed at the 'point-of-sale' and subsequent processing dependent on the physical transmission of one part to the card company. Authorisation of payments is also a significant factor with reference to central records having to be made through telephone calls from retailers to the card companies' enquiry facilities. Certain card issuers have begun to introduce more automated processes for authorisation and in some cases systems have been introduced to complete the whole transaction in one operation.

American Express, Barclays Bank and Clydesdale Bank have initiated schemes of this nature.

The American Express system has been established in conjunction with Army and Navy Stores. Within this system customers present cards which are automatically referred through the Army and Navy terminals to American Express in Brighton and then, if necessary, by satellite link to the operations centre in Phoenix, Arizona, for verification. The entire operation is achieved within seconds and minimises customer waiting time. The resultant transactions are electronically produced and require no production of the familiar flimsy vouchers.

Barclays Bank has established the 'Barclays Supercash' scheme which is centred within the Mainstop Hypermarket in Wymondham, Norfolk. This allows customers to withdraw cash from their accounts by use of either a Barclaycard or Barclaybank card. The system involves an automated authorisation process through a terminal linked by a leased line to the local Barclays branch and then to their Computer Centre at Gloucester.

Clydesdale Bank, in conjunction with British Petroleum, has established a scheme, named 'Counterplus', operating at two petrol stations in Aberdeen. By this system, a customer presents a card in payment, the verification of all relative information being obtained by linkage of the local terminal equipment into the main Clydesdale Bank terminal network. The resultant electronic transaction is automatically created and transmitted through the same medium. As with the Army and Navy stores system, there is no need for the production of flimsy vouchers—thereby streamlining the entire transmission process.

Interesting though these experiments are, they only touch the fringe of our current payment systems. The insatiable demand for cash continues. Evidence of change in the means of providing this can be seen today in almost every High Street, where banks have installed cash dispensers which operate under particular 'brand names' such as Barclaycash, Cashpoint and Servicetill. Over 2500 of these machines (often referred to in the American terminology as Automated Teller Machines—'ATMs') are now installed and every bank seems to have plans to substantially increase their present population. The majority of these machines are located through walls of bank branches and available 24 hours a day, although one bank which began by installing the machines inside their branches, with limited availability has introduced some 50 machines into major departmental stores. The largest network available throughout 24 hours at present is NatWest's Servicetill System. Their six hundredth machine was installed in May 1982.

Simple to operate through the use of a plastic card and a personal identification number, the popularity of the machines ought never to have been in doubt. The proof of their success can be seen all over the country where small queues develop throughout the prime shopping periods to withdraw cash from their bank accounts. The information relevant to the customers account is recorded by the machines, which have an on-line connection with the relevant computer system and the whole transaction is completed entirely automatically. A number of additional facilities are also available, such as balance enquiry, cheque book and statement ordering, but until more machines are installed, or quicker dispensing facilities introduced, the banks will need to consider carefully the wisdom of extending the range of services for fear of increasing the time each customer uses the machine and causing queues to lengthen to an unacceptable degree. Side-by-side with the introduction of self-service machines note counters have been installed to aid bank cashiers and many of these now help to speed up the issue of cash in the busiest bank branches.

The cheque, as has already been noted, remains an important means of effecting payment. Since 1961 we have become very familiar with the stylised characters printed along the bottom edge of our cheques. Twenty years later they still provide the means by which these cheques can be automatically handled and the accounting data recorded for debiting to the appropriate account. Yet despite the substantial investment in equipment for this operation, the clearing departments of the banks still employ a large workforce engaged on essential supporting tasks—without automation one is entitled to wonder whether a viable cheque clearing system could operate today. The validity of the technique is further illustrated by the recent moves to extend it to credit items which are exchanged between banks and form the credit clearing. For a variety of reasons little progress in automating this section of work has previously been made, but as will be seen later there is now active interest in progressing this matter.

Nevertheless, handling of paper documents and the passing of them from bank to bank and branch to branch will inevitably continue to be a cumbersome task, whatever degree of automation is introduced. Consequently the banks have attached great importance to the continuing development of the Bankers Automated Clearing Service (BACS). Established in 1967 the BACS system receives magnetic tapes from banks and customers containing debits and credits for bank accounts. The BACS computers sort the items into appropriate order for the banks to which the items are addressed and create magnetic tapes for processing by the individual banks. The whole process is virtually automatic with the minimum of manual intervention and documentary control.

The BACS system installed at Edgware by the London Clearing Banks quickly grew and for many years has been the largest operation of its kind in the world. Almost 500 million transactions were handled by the system in 1981. Some 5000 corporate customers provide magnetic tape to the BACS System. The majority of transactions comprise the regular payments (standing orders) made by banks on behalf of their customers, but a significant growth area is the salary and wages payment facility, which accounts for some 18 per cent of the total BACS volume. These are mainly monthly salary payments, but nearly half a million weekly wages are paid in this manner. The employees' accounts at the various banks are directly credited and this method must surely eventually succeed the continuing archaic and cumbersome 'wages packet'.

Similarly the introduction of direct debits has proved an attractive facility particularly for life insurance companies, local authorities, finance houses and television rental companies in respect of certain types of payment. Under this system customers allow organisations to whom they are making regular payments to originate the debits for their accounts. A magnetic tape is presented by the organisations to BACS and the various debits automatically produced for the individual customer accounts. The method is particularly suitable where amounts frequently vary, simplifying the process for the organisation, the customer and the banks.

BACS is an important factor in the banks' future automation plans and new methods of accepting data from customers are being introduced. These include direct telecommunication links and also cassette and diskette input, which make the automated facilities of BACS available to smaller businesses which do not have access to large tape producing computer systems.

Historically all these features and payment systems would have been considered the preserve of the major clearing banks, but more recently other organisations have entered the field to widen the choice available to the general public and provide competition. Perhaps this could be said to have begun with the establishment of the National Girobank in 1967. The giro system is based upon the maintenance of all accounts in a single centre located at Bootle where accounts are effectively debited and credited simultaneously. The single centre avoids the cheque and credit clearing systems operated by the clearing banks and simplifies account to account transfers. As a result the use of optical characters (rather than magnetic used by the clearing banks) has been extensively exploited. The National Girobank is the largest user of this technique in the United Kingdom.

The advent of competition has considerably blurred the demarcation lines between the traditional roles pursued by our financial institutions. building societies, seeing the need to maintain their deposits have sought to provide transmission facilities akin to those available from banks. The Trustee Savings Banks have similarly widened their facilities, with lending schemes and credit cards forming part of their customer services. The banks, too, have been alert to their customer needs and have broadened their activities which now embrace almost every financial service which can be conceived. Most recent has been the introduction of home loans for house purchase on terms which many people have found more attractive than those available from building societies. The opportunities arising from the availability of competing services must be recognised as welcome from the point of view of the consumer and are readily accepted by the established financial organisations as an exciting challenge to their future developments. In this regard information technology will play an essential part, for whilst so far we have discussed various automated payment procedures the essential prosperity of financial institutions remains dependent on their ability to attract deposits. The extensive branch networks operated by the clearing banks are an important feature and provide convenient customer access to the banking system. It is not an accident that building societies have in recent years considerably extended their number of offices and are generally open on Saturdays.

Subsequently, through its lending and investment policies, a bank deploys its deposits to ensure security to the depositor, and provide funds for the development of industries, homes and consumer goods, aiming to accomplish these objectives in a profitable manner.

The various payment systems meet the many customer needs and help to attract depositors and in this regard they form an important part of a bank's operation. Against the prime objectives of obtaining deposits and lending money, payment systems can, however, be enormously expensive to operate and consequently there is the need to ensure that full advantage is taken of new technology. A number of potential new developments are discussed later, but perhaps the most important and exciting opportunity is presented by the availability of mini-processors and associated data storage.

This equipment will enable many bank branch customer records, hitherto maintained manually in bank branches, to be automated. Thus, in conjunction with the account information held in the large central computer facilities, branch managers and staff will be able to obtain all relevant customer information through terminals linked to both local and central computer systems. In due time the laborious process of filing correspondence and retrieving records will become memories of the past, and often expensive space occupied by filing cabinets made available for a more constructive use. The use, too, of new communication services, such as Packet Switching, is intriguing the planners of future systems and many foresee that this could be the means through which all types of correspondence and statements could be delivered to the customers of the future, given the concept of terminals in every home.

'The Office of the Future' is the subject of a separate chapter in this book, but the opportunity the new technology provides to integrate the customer files in branches and the central accounting data is particularly important to the finance industry. In marketing a widening range of services and responding to the needs of customers, readily available, accurate information is essential. It would be illusory to believe that the manual methods we have known to date can for long continue to provide satisfactory records, particularly taking into account the growth in business which the financial institutions anticipate. It may therefore be assumed that rapid developments and considerable innovations will occur in this area. Already some banks have made substantial investments in word processing systems and more comprehensive schemes are being developed for early implementation.

This review of the existing development of information processing in the financial industry has tended to deal exclusively with developments in the U.K. and has not recorded overseas developments. In practice technological developments tend to be made available simultaneously all over the world and in many instances the new systems introduced into our financial institutions have been parallelled by similar organisations overseas.

Nationwide financial institutions, good communications facilities and density of population are amongst the factors which have worked to the advantage of the United Kingdom in adopting new procedures, and much of the equipment installed in the banking industry today has been manufactured within the British Isles. The large banks are, however, major institutions in the international financial market with many offices abroad in the major centres and comprehensive correspondent bank relationships with the largest banks abroad.

British banks have, therefore, strongly supported a significant development in the use of automation in international banking procedures. S.W.I.F.T. (Society for Worldwide Interbank Financial Telecommunication), was established by the international banking community as a co-operative in 1973 and became operational in 1977. The S.W.I.F.T. system now extends to 39 countries and over 900 banks are active members of the organisation. S.W.I.F.T. operates through three switching centres located in Belgium, Holland and the United States, with regional processors in the majority of the member countries. Over 250,000 payment messages a day representing a very significant amount of money are transmitted between the member banks in a secure and controlled manner. The S.W.I.F.T. system represents an impressive achievement in international co-operation, and provides a system which enables payments for international trade to be made far more effectively than previous methods which relied upon telex and mail.

In the U.K. a new inter bank system to automate payments with same-day settlement is currently being developed. This is known as C.H.A.P.S. (Clearing House Automated Payments System). Identical processors will be installed in each designated Settlement Bank. These will communicate with each other through British Telecom's Packet Switching Network. However, once the transfer of the payment message from one Settlement Bank to another is completed the design of the system is such that each bank can determine the manner in which the item is subsequently processed. Therefore, whilst providing for the formality and standard procedures necessary for effective inter-bank exchange of information, the system allows the major U.K. banks to offer competitive facilities to overseas banks in London who can obtain access to the C.H.A.P.S. System through any one of these Settlement Banks. Automatic links between a bank's main processor and the S.W.I.F.T. network are likely to be developed, thus providing a complete link between banks overseas and the London financial market. A similar system, styled C.H.I.P.S. (Clearing House Inter-bank Payment System) is in operation in New York. The C.H.A.P.S. system is expected to come into operation in London during 1983.

C.H.A.P.S. primarily is an automatic system for the transmission of large payments. It is designed to serve the needs of companies and other large institutions. Companies need to hold large amounts of cash to cover their day-to-day operations and to provide for unexpected changes in business conditions.

Greater uncertainty in the economy and higher interest rates have meant that for the company treasurer there are considerable benefits to be gained from the effective utilisation of cash resources. Today's company treasurer is concerned with corporate cash management, with reducing overall borrowing costs and other bank charges, with maximising the profitable use of surplus funds, and with safeguarding the company against currency exposure risks. These activities naturally become more complex for the multi-national company with world-wide operations, and the treasurer is now looking to banks to assist by the provision of a corporate cash management service. With today's technology in the financial world the banks are in a position to respond.

In the United States many banks already offer various automated services directed at accelerating the transmission of payments, centralising bank balances at a focal point within the company, reporting account balances and transactions to the company treaurer, and also enabling the treasurer to initiate movement of funds. To date these services have been geared mostly to the specific needs of the domestic United States market; however, many British and European companies are beginning to recognise the value and importance of these services. Consequently banks in Britain and Europe are actively engaged in examining ways in which they can respond to their customers' requirements.

In developing these services a bank has to decide what type of information or 'product' is required by the corporate customer, on which computer system the data-base is kept, and where the processing is carried out. Banks may develop their own systems for processing and holding files to which customers are given access. Alternatively, third party companies may be engaged who have already developed specialist packages and the banks' customers could be linked directly to these systems.

A reliable, secure, efficient network is also an essential requirement for a cash management system. The bank may rely on its own inter-branch network, or again may utilise third party commercial networks often provided by those specialist companies already mentioned, or utilise its S.W.I.F.T. connection. Information will need to be easily entered into the network by the appropriate parties. This could originate from the bank's own computer centre, a local banking branch, a correspondent bank, or the customer himself.

It would appear likely that in view of the more immediate need for the banks to develop and provide effective corporate cash management services in the short term, if they are new to this field, they will initially purchase the packages provided by the specialist companies and market them under the bank's own name. Once a bank has established a range of customer services then a planned in-house development of new products and services which utilise the bank's own computer and network resources could well be justified.

Private customers also, who issue vast numbers of cheques and require regular sums of cash, will continue to see significant changes in the way banks deal with their accounts. Today much effort is expended in moving millions of cheques and credits around the country. Considerable interest has been devoted to examining ways in which this can be reduced. The objective is to transmit the relevant information whilst leaving the paper behind at the first branch it arrived at. This process, termed 'Truncation' does not yet look like being adopted by the banks in the immediate future, but a number of limited schemes are in operation and some intriguing pilot experiments are being conducted. Certain legal issues need to be resolved, however, and sound technical solutions have yet to appear.

Two possibilities suggest themselves as the most likely at the moment. The first of these capitalises upon the characters along the bottom edge of cheques and credits, using low-cost reading equipment for installation at branch counters. The accounting information is then transmitted to the banks' central computer centres for applying to the individual customers accounts. A deficiency of this concept however, is that the non-encoded information, (the date, customer's signature, payee's name) cannot be transmitted. If this constraint continues and needs to be overcome a new technique known as 'Image Processing' offers a means. Effectively a picture or 'image' of the document is taken in the branch where an item first enters the banking system. The image can then be transmitted to the central system, and handled in a completely automatic way until finally the complete picture of the original document can be displayed on a screen or printed, possibly as part of a customer statement. During this process the appropriate accounting information can be extracted (again automatically) to credit or debit the customer's account. Present enthusiasm for this technique is, however, tempered by the costs of transmission, the storage space required within the central system to record the images, and the cost of the reading devices themselves.

Whatever the future may hold for 'Image Processing' it is not likely to make an immediate impact and hence the need to continue to exploit established techniques and practices. Consequently, the banks are planning to introduce automation to credits in a similar manner to the way cheques are processed. An important difference however is the acceptability of optical characters either in total or in a mixed line with magnetic characters. Whilst the National Girobank has been a large and successful user of optical reading, apart from a limited number of applications the banks have hitherto tended to ignore this method.

What cannot be ignored however is the banks' interest in point-of-sale payment systems. At the end of 1981 after turning down an earlier proposal the banks announced their intention of going ahead with plans for the introduction of a new payments system based on the use of terminals at the point-of-sale.

When such a system is introduced, transactions in retail stores can be instantly converted into electronic information and transmitted to banks, credit card companies and any other institutions which may join the system. Simply and quickly the financial side of our purchases will be completed and the goods will be ours. In this electronic world of tomorrow there would be no cash, no cheques, no giro transfer forms, no multipart credit card forms—only terminals and plastic cards. Whether such a complete revolution is likely in the lifetime of present generations must be the subject of some conjecture, nevertheless technically the means exist today to enable such a world to operate and few should doubt that the first steps are surely going to be taken soon to extend the initial experiments which are already operating. Vitally important to the success of an electronic funds system is the role of the retailers themselves and the banks will need to ensure through discussion and consultation that their proper needs are adequately protected. Space and speed are both essential considerations when one considers retail counters and the paying process. The financing of any scheme is an equally daunting issue and legal considerations of allocating liability and privacy ensure that the banks' policy committee recently established will have full and complicated agendas for their study.

For those who do not find the hustle and bustle of a visit to the high street shops an attractive prospect, banking in the next decade may well offer a tempting alternative. The introduction of Prestel and the intention to establish cable television provide the prospect that through televisions and telephones direct contact with banks' computers can be established. Add the display of goods on the television screen and a shopping expedition of the future is simply relaxing in a favourite armchair. This exciting prospect is attracting considerable interest in the United States, but the very limited number of private Prestel sets so far installed in Britain has to date appeared to have led to banks in this country adopting a 'wait and see' approach. A number of practical and legal issues will need to be resolved before a full-scale 'home banking' facility is realistic, but perhaps the most crucial question of all will be over the issue of customer identification. Some will doubt that the personal identification numbers (PIN's) used in today's cash dispensers in closed bank networks will be adequate in the more public forum in which 'home banking' will prosper. The debate will be fascinating, but whatever its outcome there is no doubt that universal acceptance of new methods of processing and the use of information technology will depend on public confidence that the proper measure of privacy is maintained and adequate security provided. However, we only delude ourselves if we believe new technology will replace systems which were absolutely private and completely secure. In many respects access to computer files can be more effectively restricted and controlled than with conventional systems which they replace. Those implementing new systems need to ensure that this is the case.

The nature of the information flow and its sheer volume, of which this chapter has given some indication, will result in an increasing number of distributed systems being installed and lead to much more extensive use of telecommunication facilities within financial establishments, between their branches and to their customers. The opportunity for utilising new facilities such as high speeds of transmission provided by optical fibres and satellites and the services of Prestel is now emerging quickly. Liberalisation of the 'Post Office Act' and the introduction of competition to British Telecom is indeed a timely action.

The extension of on-line authorisation and record keeping systems and the interaction which these require between user and machine perhaps begins to foresee the demise of batch processing. The traditional financial systems which collected data in prime shift and processed the account records throughout the night will not meet the needs of new electronic funds transfer systems where most activity will take place during shop opening hours. If the banks continue to see increased volumes they need to recognise that those volumes will need to be processed in a much more concentrated period than has previously been necessary.

While an on-line real time system should perhaps be available 24 hours a day, its most active use will be restricted to less than a third of that time. The introduction of new systems is only successful if the concerns of both staff and customers are effectively addressed. This book highlights many developments which illustrate the advancement of technology and the likely acceleration in the speed of change. The financial world has an enviable record in the satisfactory implementation of new systems to date, and those employed in the industry have welcomed the changes which have occurred. There is no reason to believe that the future will be different but management will need to continue to ensure that the proposed changes are properly understood and the appropriate level of re-training provided. The media, too, have a responsibility in recognising the desirability for this country's financial institutions to continue to lead the world in innovative systems. Articles in the press and presentations on radio and television need to promote public understanding of both the opportunities and the constraints which new developments create.

Finally, the role of government may be most crucial of all. In designating 1982 as Information Technology Year it has given a public and welcome impetus to future thinking. To encourage but *not* to prescribe and *not* to constrain is surely the proper action for government to take. It needs to allow organisations to show enterprise and take initiatives which are not hindered by control or threatened by bureaucracy. The range of financial services available in this country is extensive and many competitive alternatives ensure a wide consumer choice. The exploitation of information technology as this chapter has attempted to show suggests that this will continue.

The consumers, not governments, will finally determine which services meet their future needs, which ones are preferred to old established facilities. There is every indication that they will have a rich choice.

7

An Application of Information Technology in The Office of the Future

RICHARD BROOKS

Technology Correspondent, The Sunday Times

IMAGINE, if you can, 1,000,000,000,000 pages of paper. Laid end-to-end they would be about 200 million miles long, or the distance from the earth to the sun and back again. That is the amount of paper used each year in the offices of the world. Some read, some useful, some stored and some thrown away. In fact a great deal thrown away, partly because it is fairly disposable in content and partly because there is no place to keep it.

The office of today is a forest of paper, populated by an ever growing number of humans. In Britain twenty years ago, there were five million office workers. Now there are more than seven million, or 40 per cent of the workforce. In the United States, the growth in numbers has been even more marked. Twenty two million office workers in 1960, and now 40 million, or 45 per cent of the workforce.

There are 1.7 million offices in Britain. About 95 per cent have fewer than 50 workers. If there is such a thing, the average office is probably up on the second floor of a building with a staff of about ten. A boss, two or three manager types, three secretaries/typists, a switchboard operator/receptionist and a sales representative. Between them, there is an antiquated and very limited telephone exchange, three electric typewriters, one manual, and a photocopier. And that is about it. Total office equipment value, if you leave out the desks, chairs and filing cabinets, is around £6000, or the cost of a secretary's annual salary.

A small factory would also probably have an adjoining office.

However, that factory, while it probably employed not that many more workers, would certainly have spent considerably more on its capital equipment. On average, the office has less than £1000 worth of capital equipment invested per worker. It is not unusual to find investment of between £15,000 and £20,000 of capital equipment per worker in manufacturing industry.

As the office population has increased, and the factory population fallen, so the productivity of the office worker has only risen by four per cent in the past ten years, against 80 per cent for the factory worker. Most of this increase is due to the large amount of new equipment put in the factory.

The case for improvements in the office is almost a foregone conclusion. The grounds for moving towards greater automation and thereby more efficiency and productivity are obvious. The Information Technology 1982 committee's definition of the office of the future is as good a dictum to be followed. "The use of computers, microelectronics and telecommunications to store, obtain and send information in the form of pictures, words and numbers more reliably, quickly and economically."

Before looking at that ideal, it is necessary to examine why today's office still has its heart in the past. Charles Dickens' might not feel too out of place in many of today's offices. The quill pen might have gone, but the bought ledger book and old desk are still there. Two of the most vital pieces of office equipment, the typewriter and telephone were both introduced in the 1870s, the same decade as Dicken's death.

While I presume no office has a typewriter or telephone 100 years old, many are at least 30 or 40 years old. Many Strowger electro-mechanical telephone exchanges, invented in the 1890s, still remain, some of them installed during the 1930s. Telephone handsets, almost as old, still exist. Although many secretaries today have electric typewriters, manual ones, some made in the 1950s, remain common place.

While comparatively very little has been spent on new office equipment in recent years, the cost of maintaining the office has itself gone up considerably. In the United States, management consultants, Booz, Allen and Hamilton, reckon that offices cost $800 billion to maintain in 1980. Three-quarters of that was spent on workers' salaries.

Other office costs are frighteningly high as well. It will cost about £4 to get a single page typed, and £1 to get it photocopied. The Civil Service, which discovered these statistics in a recent report, looked at whether it would be worthwhile getting word-processors for 30,000 secretarial staff. The report concluded that productivity increases of up to 72 per cent would be required to justify replacing electric typewriters with word processors. They based this reasoning on an analysis that word processors cost around £7000 and electric typewriters £500. Yet, such a simplistic approach does not tell the whole story.

Typists do not like sitting down all day banging out letters, particularly when it is the same, or very similar letter. It is reckoned that a typist anyway will only spend about 15 per cent of the day actually typing. Administration takes up to 25 per cent. She is away from her desk about a fifth of the time, and sits at her desk doing nothing for 10 per cent, the same amount of time she spends on the telephone.

One must not blame the poor typist, her boss is just as bad. He might like to believe that he spends most of his time on great thoughts and plans, and in important meetings. Not at all. His productive 'think time' comes out at about 30 per cent of his day, broken down between creating documents, analysis and reading. Meetings, many unproductive, take up nearly half his day. A quarter of the day is totally wasted, much of it waiting for a vital telephone call, letter or meeting, or just looking for information, not at his finger tips. For all that lack of productivity he gets a salary on average between twice and three times as much as his secretary's. It means that about 75 per cent of total office costs are spent keeping all those unproductive and well-paid managerial and executive workers.

All those reams of paper around the office must also be cut down in size. The Yankee Group management consultants reckon that every American office worker has on averge eight filing cabinets. He adds about 25 per cent more paper to that file each year, throwing out only 15 per cent. The office worker also makes about 25 telephone calls a day, many of them unproductive.

In Britain, British Telecom itself admits that 25 per cent of all calls are either engaged or get no reply. Another 10 per cent are not connected for other reasons, such as wrong numbers or line failure. Almost a half of international calls are either engaged or get no reply.

Even the calls which get through are often less than useful because the person wanted is not there, or can not give the required information. All in all, it probably means that only about one in three calls is totally successful.

If you complete that telephone call, and then ask to be sent a letter confirming the details of your conversation by post, it could easily take four days to receive it. The manager will eventually ask his secretary to type out the letter he dictates. She then puts it in the external post tray. A messenger comes along and takes it to the post room. It will be franked second class because of the firm's economy measures. Two days in the post, before it arrives at its destination. Up through the internal post system, onto the secretary's desk and eventually to her boss. A word processor with electronic mail would have done it all in minutes rather than days.

However slow offices are in adopting automation, nearly all surveys show that managers and secretaries want improved equipment and believe it will lead to better efficiency. Booz, Allen and Hamilton found that four out of five executives believe office automation improves decision making. Two-thirds think it raises productivity. Yet only just over half of the executives believed that it would improve the productivity of their clerical staff.

In Britain consultants Urwick Nexos (now called Eosys) last year carried out a survey among 300 companies into the benefits of office automation. Nine out of ten managers saw 'improved management effectiveness' as the main benefit. Unlike their American colleagues, 85 per cent thought the clerical worker's productivity would benefit. The same proportion thought that their company would get some economic gain. The British manager has either more faith in office automation than his American counterpart, or he has yet to use much of it.

The Urwick survey then asked if the companies were going to buy more modern office equipment over the next year. Nearly two thirds said they would spend more on microcomputers; 58 per cent more on word processors; 42 per cent on executive terminals and management workstations; 34 per cent on microfilm. However, less than one in five planned to spend more on electronic mail, viewdata, message switching or facsimile. As a general rule, the larger firms consulted said they would be increasing in real terms their expenditure on office automa-

Hardware orientation [handwritten margin note]

tion. More than three quarters of those with more than 50,000 employees will be increasing their budget, but only a third of firms with 50 staff or less will be.

When managers were asked what was the major problem with buying new office equipment, most said they were worried about compatibility. In other words they wanted to ensure that the micro-computer could 'talk' to the word processor, and then 'talk' to the mainframe computer. There were other worries about compatibility between intelligent copiers, facsimile machines and telephone exchanges. Cost was only the secondary worry, though many said prices would have to fall by up to 50 per cent before they would put in new equipment. It seems that some might not have noticed that hardware prices are now falling considerably, and will continue to do so, at least in real terms.

Any firms now thinking about buying or renting new office automation equipment have to think hard and deep. They will be confronted with an array of alluring advertising in the press, in magazines and on television. Their offices will be inundated with glossy brochures and mail shots. Bright eyed salesmen will knock at their door telling them that this word processor or that facsimile machine is vital to the survival of their company. Believe it or not, there are now more than 100 different firms offering word processors in Britain. That is far more than makes of soap powder, motor cars or television sets.

Two major problems face any firm about to take the plunge into the office of the future. First, are the firm's bosses getting the right information to take major decisions on buying new office equipment? Until very recently, it was left to the data processing manager to order computing equipment. There is sometimes an office equipment manager, but, all too often, he has just been used to buying fairly non-technical equipment such as electric typewriters. Firms must not be blinded by over-technical advice from their data processing departments, or the lack of knowledge of the office equipment manager. Urwick was encouraged to find that one in four firms it surveyed had in the past year appointed a person specifically to look after office automation.

The second problem is that the technology of office equipment is changing so fast that firms are either holding off buying, while waiting for the best product to make itself established, or purchasing in a rush and then having to leave the equipment unused in a corner.

What then should firms buy if they want to turn their office into an office of the future, capable of handling all the information which flows in and out of the company in the most cost-effective way. The Urwick survey said managers were going to spend more on microcomputers than any other office product. Not so long ago, the computer was hidden in the bowels of the office, a very private machine which only the data processing manager and systems analyst knew about. It was huge, and gobbled up batches of information brought down to it from the offices above. Gradually, though, the computer got smaller and friendlier. Its veil of secrecy fell away, as the microcomputer crept into offices.

The big breakthrough has been the microcomputer or desk-top computer. In 1978, general purpose computers represented 10 per cent of computers sold, small business systems 60 per cent, mini computers 22 per cent and desk-top 8 per cent. By 1983, desk-top will account for 56 per cent, mini computers 10 per cent, small business systems 32 per cent, and general purpose just 2 per cent. In the 1970s, firms such as Commodore and Apple pioneered the desk-top computer. Other computer firms, such as IBM or Digital Equipment, more used to selling big machines, eventually realised there was an enormous demand for micros, and so they jumped on the unstoppable band-wagon.

At the simplest level the small computer can carry out accounting tasks, payrolls, VAT, sales orders and inventories, usually on pre-written software. Financial modelling can be carried out with more sophisticated machines. The great plus about micros is that they can be used by managers with no background in computing. The computer's friendliness makes it a management tool, particularly in small offices. It can for instance save on the services of an accountant, and cut down much-needed management time.

However, do not expect to be without teething problems. A recent survey by the University of Lancaster into the use of small computers in small firms found that 25 of the companies sampled had installation difficulties. Nearly 60 of them had either software or hardware problems in the first six months. And yet, comments the survey sadly,

60 of the 100 companies bought without first seeing the system working, and only 33 carried out a formal feasibility study before buying. Ironically, most firms said they were happy with their computers, particularly those experienced users who tailored their own software, and used it for management accountancy or professional special applications. Firms told the University of Lancaster survey that a small computer improved information processing, planning, control, as well as working conditions and procedures.

If the micro and small computer is essentially a management tool, then the word processor has by and large been the preserve of the secretary. Yet the word processor is also the most likely first machine which many firms will use on their way to becoming an office of the future. Initially many firms make the mistake of treating the word processor as a glorified typewriter. It can and does make typing a lot easier, but it also has many more functions.

At the start of 1982 Britain only had about 40,000 stand alone word processors, against 600,000 throughout the whole of the world. Word processor popularity is growing fast. Pactel consultants say that the annual world-wide growth rate will average about 40 per cent between 1982 and 1984, compared with data equipment growth rates of 15 per cent. Major word processor makers, such as Wang, Xerox and IBM, say that in 1981 volume growth rates grew by 65 per cent.

The great advantage of a word processor is that it is a screen based system. If properly used the word processor is an electronic typewriter, small computer, electronic filing cabinet and message receiver all rolled into one. A good word processor should make letter or document typing a joy. Editing text on screen, inserting new material, deleting old, correcting spelling and adding new paragraphs become simple.

A word processor moves text in much the same way that a calculator or computer juggles with numbers. Now that word processors are beginning to pick up sales, even in backward Britain, prices are plummeting. One bought in early 1982 would cost about a third less than one bought 12 months earlier. Price-wise, a line of word processing already costs less than a standard electric typewriter. A stand alone word processor now costs about three times as much as the average memory typewriter, though it has many more functions.

More and more firms are using word processors together, in much the same way that microcomputers are being used together. In an even larger system, the word processor can share and be linked with a more powerful computer. They can also share central facilities like memories and printers. The memory of many word processors today is very considerable, holding quite easily up to 10,000 words in the stand-alone itself. If necessary floppy discs can hold much more information to be loaded into the word processor when needed.

An advanced word processor, which can act as a typewriter, computer and message sender, will become an ideal management tool. As word processors develop they will use advanced microchip technology to give them more computing power. That will mean the word processor carrying out specific tasks such as sales forecasts, rather than having to carry out time-consuming programming. This will all make the word processor more likely to become the dominant machine in the office of the future. The word processor is also the likely focus of what is becoming known as the work-station—a glorified desk on which sits an advanced word processor and telecommunications equipment. It will take over from today's desk, full of drawers and cluttered up with typewriter, phones, while surrounded by filing cabinets.

The priorities for any management work-station are that it must be multi-functional and user-friendly. A manager will also want it to be as similar to his existing non-electronic desk. If he is used to a note-pad, in and out trays, then his work-station screen must be capable of being divided into sections. Any manager uses lots of information, pieces of paper and documents, all together. His work-station must let him carry on these multifunctional tasks. The management work-station will be a word processor for memos and documents; an electronic mail system; a filing system; a dictionary. It must have easy access to data-bases, having extra peripherals attached and communicate with other devices. The manager does not want to have to programme his work-station. All information and tasks must be available at the touch of a key, or the use of a cursor, such as the so-called mouse of Xerox's Star system.

The American consultancy, International Resource Development, believes the electronic office will evolve in three stages. Stage one comes with the introduction of work-station equipment into the office. Two, the connection of work-stations via local networks. Three, the expansion of local networks into the distributed office.

The local area network (LAN), where products of the office of the future are connected together, means that different people and offices can all have access to the same information. The LAN will increasingly be fundamental to the electronic office. International Resource Development, in a report published in April 1982, estimates that within ten years more than six million American executives, managers, professionals and support personnel will be using work-stations attached to a LAN. Most will have instant access to millions of pages of electronically stored information at the push of a button. All will be able to move memos and documents around in minutes. Location and distance are irrelevant in the networked office. It does not matter whether users are in the same room, building, town or even country.

The local area network will be the linchpin in many offices of the future. A manager in, for example, the Manchester office of a company can put a memo or graphic design on his word processor, and through the LAN within seconds it will arrive in the Birmingham office with a coded instruction to go to the relevant recipient. He in turn looks at the word processor screen to see if there is any information for him, and calls it up. He can just look at it, ask for a print-out or file it electronically.

The battle for the LAN market is already hotting up. The problem is that competing types of LANs all make different claims. Some are so-called bus systems, others ring, others star. Some are base-band cable, taking mainly data, others broad-band, also take voice and video. Currently the most widely installed LAN system is the Arc, developed by the Texas firm Datapoint. It has more customers because its Arc system is ideal for linking its own minicomputers and word processors. But Datapoint's problems are first that it is a comparatively small firm, and second that it can only join Datapoint products. Bigger firms like Xerox, a later starter, realise this. Its Ethernet LAN started selling in the United States in 1981, and in Britain this year. Xerox wants Ethernet to become the world's standard, and is letting other firms build Ethernet. Technically Ethernet and Arc are bus networks, using open ended coaxial cable to which terminals are connected. Both are also base-band. However broad-band cable proponents like Wang claim its Wangnet will eventually win because of its greater capacity. But broad-band is also considerably more expensive.

To confuse matters further, there are also ring and star LANs. Ring systems include Prime's Ringnet, Logica's Polynet and Xionics' Xinet. They are called ring, because the cable goes round in a joined loop, with individual terminals connected to the loop. Other LANs, such as those developed by North American firms Rolm and Northern Telecom, plus Britain's Plessey, are based on digital PABXs. In these star systems, a number of cables radiate out from the central exchange.

As with so much electronic office equipment, the pros and cons are hard to evaluate. Ethernet's problem at present is that voice cannot be mixed with data. On the other hand it is cheap to run and can link up with equipment from other suppliers. Rings, which can operate over greater distances, have the disadvantage that any fault on the ring can mean a complete shutdown. Star LANs, based on the PABX, are simple and low cost, but the information fed through is limited and not very fast.

The PABX and telecommunications equipment are of course in many ways the most crucial elements of any office. Some office workers will literally spend more than three-quarters of their day on the telephone. Most of it, one hopes, not on personal calls! Very, very few office workers do not use the telephone. Because it is so much used it will always have a vital function in any electronic office. This is why firms such as Plessey and ITT are arranging their LANs around the PABX.

Managers in particular love voice communication. Perhaps, as their secretaries might say, it is simply that they love the sound of their own voices. If only voice command could activate a desk top terminal or word processor. Do not worry because it will. The Japanese are working on it. Philips is developing a typewriter which types on voice command. Britain's Logica has just developed a speech recognition system which British Telecom is to try out.

For the present though we just want a better telephone system. British Telecom rightly received considerable stick for its appalling waiting lists for telephone connections, notably in the City of London. However, it did respond. At the end of 1980 the London demand list for new telephones was 40,000. A year later it was down to 11,000. The wait for PABXs was more than a year, by 1982 it was a few weeks. A private line can now be put in within 24 hours, against one year in 1980.

Despite these improvements, Britain's telephone system has not been upgraded as fast as most in Western Europe and the United States. Now

BT is gradually putting in a digital network, run by System X computer controlled exchanges. Optical fibre cables on trunk routes, which are better for transmitting data, are also slowly being laid. A rival telecommunications network, run by a consortium headed by Cable & Wireless, should link up seven major English cities within two years.

Telecommunications liberalisation, following the passing of the Telecommunications Act in 1981, will mean better equipment, notably of PABXs. New exchanges are computer controlled and can take both voice and data. Liberalisation also means new types of handsets, call analysis equipment, answering phones, car radios and cordless phones. It has also made British Telecom a far more market-oriented organisation, with a new sales force of 600 just to sell business systems.

Many other technological advances will bring the office of the future nearer to reality. One component of that office will be an electronic mail system. At its simplest it is no more than a glorified telex sent over a word processor. More sophisticated systems will have a store and forward capability, and list-based distribution. Electronic mail is most cost-effective when used out of office hours. Sent over the cheap-rate telephone line between word processors in different offices, it could soon prove a real rival to the postman.

The PTT version of electronic mail, known as Teletex, will also have a greater role as it takes over from the slower and more limited telex. Several pages can be transferred during one call. The pages themselves are typed into a word processor and linked by the telephone line to other word processors. British Telecom is launching its Teletex service this year. It already has an electronic mail system Telecom Gold, plus Dialcom for intra-company use. Firms like Shell International, Imperial Group and Philips are already using it.

Viewdata, or videotex as it is called internationally, is quite well known to many managers. The user is linked by telephone and a television screen to a computer base. British Telecom's version, Prestel, has had slower than hoped for sales since it was first introduced in 1979. The advantages are access to specialised information 'pages', particularly of news and finance. The disadvantage is that until very recently only British Telecom's computer could be accessed. From April 1982, at first on a very limited basis, Prestel users will be able to go through a so-called gateway and link into other organisations' computers.

Some firms, such as British Leyland, Debenhams and the Stock Exchange, are using private viewdata systems. A BL dealer at, for example, the showroom in Plymouth can find out immediately whether a specific car is in the showroom at Bristol through private viewdata. It saves having to telephone around all dealers in his vicinity.

As we become more used to the television-type screen, so forms of communications like teleconferencing will grow. So far expense has limited use. Another problem with, for example, British Telecom's Confravision is that individuals have had to go to special studios. But this is changing. In the United States, firms are setting up private teleconferencing. The computer firm Datapoint, which has four offices spread over a few miles in San Antonio, uses teleconferencing daily. A television set, which has a built-in camera, is placed in executives' offices. Whoever speaks has his picture on the screen, except that in the speaker's office the previous speaker is shown. Camera quality is so good that douments can be shown up clearly. The possibilities of saving on business travel with teleconferencing are enormous, especially with the use of satellite teleconferencing. Whether business-men, who usually see travel as a perk, will be so keen to adopt teleconferencing and stay back in the office is open to some doubt though.

The once humble typewriter also has its role in the office of the future. First there was the manual, then the electric and now the electronic. In simple terms it is midway between the electric and the word processor. At the start of 1980 there were less than 1000 electronic typewriters in Britain, rising to 24,000 by the end of the year. A year later there were more than 50,000, slightly more than the British population of word processors. At retail prices of between £800 and £2,000 they are considerably cheaper than word processors, and for many people the electronic typewriter will be a useful stepping stone to the more powerful word processor. Electronic typewriters can also be linked into LANs.

The copier is another machine which like the typewriter has been around for ages. Stories about it breaking down are common enough, though usually it is the user who mistreats it. At the top end, firms like

Xerox have dominated for years, though the Japanese, notably Canon, Ricoh and Sharp, are coming on fast at the lower end of the market. As competition continues, prices have tumbled, which can only be good news for customers. The main consideration is whether to have one large and fast copier for multi-runs, or several small ones. More sophisticated copiers can scan pages by laser and print out at a different terminal. Here there are obvious similarities with facsimile. The so-called intelligent copier can reproduce information stored in a computer or word processor. It works by de-coding data into a page image. In several ways it is like a word processor, especially as it has a memory and sorts out text. The results though are high quality paper copies, not screen pages.

While the office of the future is trying to get rid of some of the billions of pages of paper cluttering desks and filing cabinets, it will not cut out the need for information. Far from it. However, other ways will have to be found for storing it. Computers and word processors are one thing and microfilm and microfiche are another, especially as storage can cost about 30 times less than it does on paper.

The relationship between microfilm and the computer is also growing steadily. About a quarter of the pages of computer output in the United States go straight onto microfilm or fiche, on what is known as computer output microfilm(COM). Technically it is quite possible to get data from word processors straight onto microfilm. Hard and floppy discs also store very considerable amounts of data. The optical disc which can store 25,000 pages of paper also has huge potential. Philips, which has pioneered the laser optical disc, has the Megadoc. This can scan a page of paper within a second, and then transform the information onto the laser recorder, which makes the discs.

So much for the products. Many firms trying them out tend to be either computer and electronic firms, which sometimes have a vested interest, or large firms with cash to spend. Most who have taken the plunge tend, quite rightly, to do it slowly and piecemeal. Try one product out first, see if it makes your office more efficient, and go on from there.

This is just what the Chemical Bank is doing. The bank is already well advanced in using technology for its international banking and finance, and decided some of the same skills could be used to transfer its European administrative headquarters from London to Cardiff. An integral part of the system, which makes the London and Cardiff offices almost as one, will be a digital telecommunications link to carry data, voice and image. Eventually 240 individual desk-top terminals in Cardiff and 100 in London, where the finance department will stay, will be connected into the one network.

Several of Britain's biggest employers have been in the vanguard of the office revolution. Unilever, ICI and BP have all had word processors for some years. Unilever even invented its own word processor, the Unicom, in the 1960s. The company estimates that word processors have raised typists output by three-fold. ICI had its first word processors in 1976. Since then it has spent about £2.5 million on them, using three different makes. About half of ICI's word processors are stand-alone, the rest linked. Both managers and secretaries use them. ICI has set up a corporate office technology panel to encourage an effective and economic policy for the introduction of the office of the future.

BP Oil was one of the first firms to set up a local area network at its Hemel Hempstead accounting and computer headquarters. It was the first customer for the tiny British firm Xionics. After starting with six linked word processors, by early 1982 there were eighteen. Word processing, electronic mail and filing are the main uses. The BP LAN is used by managers, though most, it must be said, have a background in computers and are not frightened of technology. Xionics has since installed its LAN at firms like Littlewoods and Allied Breweries.

Xerox's Ethernet was first installed in Britain at Sun Life Assurance in Bristol in March 1982. Nine word processors, a laser printer and two small computers are linked into the system. Sun Life sees its Ethernet LAN first of all as a clerical tool, rather than a management one. The Greater London Council and Chevron are also installing Ethernets.

There is of course resistance to the office of the future, and there will be for some time. The first organised protest came from the Association of Scientific, Technical and Managerial Staff under the leadership of Clive Jenkins and Barry Sherman. They have written several books and pamphlets voicing their concern about office automation and the effect on jobs. That feeling is still there, though ASTMS does not reject technology for technology's sake.

It must be said that the introduction of word processors or electronic typewriters obviously speeds up clerical work, and makes it unnecessary to employ so many typists. That can mean redundancy, or firms not taking on so many typists. On the other hand it can mean freeing a typist or secretary from the tedious task of banging away hour after hour on a virtually identical letter, when a word processor or electronic typewriter can do the job in a fraction of the time. Electronic mail will also cut down the need for so many internal messengers, as well as having some effect on the Post Office itself. But it does speed up the sending of information, and that should be the major reason for using it. Even so very considerable thought must be given to jobs. It is too glib just to say that people will have more leisure time and freedom because of office automation.

Consideration must also be given to possible health hazards in the office of the future. Some tests have shown that word processors can affect the eyes. Recently work by the Swedes has shown that if the screen words and numbers are brown rather than green then it is just as easy to read, and far more soothing on the eye. Some modern office furniture, notably chairs, leave much to be desired, and can cause painful backs. The United States has some very advanced seats, particularly for sitting for many hours at a word processor.

Research in America shows that in the past year or so it is the manager and executive rather than the clerical and secretarial staff who are wanting to use new office automation products. They have become 'trendy'. Many managers will also have back at their home a personal computer, a video and cable TV. They have got used to electronic gadgetry, especially if they are under 40 years old. Because they are used to twiddling with knobs and buttons at home, and watching a visual display screen, they can easily do the same at the office. The day is coming when one will feel left out without a work-station, particularly if a colleague has one. Why haven't I? What have I done wrong?

Yet the office of the future will only become the office of today through a process of stealth and seepage. Nobody in their right mind should buy an entire electronic office at once—an off the peg buy. Wise buyers will ignore, or at least ponder, many of the tempting offers from manufacturers of office equipment. Instead they will buy one product, see how it works and more importantly see if the outlay has improved office productivity. You can then add, and add again. Manufacturers these days offer a family of goods to grow up with. However, any advice that the paperless office will come about overnight, itself deserves to be thrown straight into the wastepaper basket.

Part Three

8

Mass Communication

J B COWIE*

*Head of Long Range and Strategic Studies Division,
British Telecom*

Introduction

This chapter discusses the impact of developments in information technology on the residential customer. The emphasis will be on services which depend on a communications infrastructure rather than on self contained products.

A list of services which are feasible is not very helpful without some indication of the economic, technical, behavioural and political factors which will affect their rate of take up. Some consideration will also be given to what is known about residential information needs, to potential problems which need to be considered, to the links between residential and business developments and to the state of play in the United States.

Consumer Attitudes

One suspects that many consumers are sceptical that information technology developments will have much impact on themselves, although they may mean more for their children. If anything their attitude may well be mildly hostile since the emotions are more easily

* The views expressed are those of the author and are not necessarily shared by British Telecom.

aroused by visions of machines taking over human functions and by '1984' than by the benefits these developments might bring. They are suspicious that the 'enthusiasts' will overestimate the attractiveness of their offerings and the rate of take up when, for example, less than half the population have bank accounts. The challenge is to be able to offer new services which will prove attractive to enough customers to be commercially viable. For many of the potential new services this will depend on improvements in the communications infrastructure.

Infrastructure Developments

The general public are familiar with a number of communication services—television, the telephone, newspapers and the mail. In the past these have been conceptually and technically separate. Each makes a contribution to one or more of the three primary objectives of communications, to 'inform', to 'entertain' and to 'educate'. However, more recently this separation is breaking down. The telecommunications network is being used to link customers to information in computer centres with the output displayed on adapted television sets. The same sets can display information provided by the broadcasting organisations exploiting spare capacity in their systems. The Government has given the go ahead for direct broadcasting from satellite in 1986 and is considering the liberalisation of wideband systems over cable which could support both broadcasting and telecommunications services, and new devices such as video-cassettes and video-discs are coming on the market which could complement or compete with other ways of delivering information services.

Hence organisations which in the past have had a distinctive role in communications are having to reassess how these technical developments might affect the economics of their existing services and what new services they might be well placed to provide. An obvious example of a possible threat is the potential impact of 'electronic mail' on the Post Office.

The Development of an Infrastructure—
The Example of Prestel

British Telecom pioneered the linking of television sets to computer centres via the telecommunications network. The BT public system called Prestel has led to similar systems in other countries and private systems are mushrooming. The current statistics for Prestel are given in Table 1:

Table 1:   Prestel Statistics

Major information providers	180
Some act as brokers for smaller information providers	700 sub-information providers
Pages of information in data-base	222,000
Capacity of system	500,000 pages
Approved adapted television sets including adaptors for existing receivers	over 70
Number of customers — business — residential	13,000 2,000
Total accesses to the system	108 million

Although these statistics are in advance of anywhere else in the world, many may regard the take up as disappointing particularly in the residential sector although the emphasis of Prestel Marketing has now switched to the business community. They may not be surprised that the public is hesitant to pay for information on the wide range of subjects offered by Prestel—travel timetables and holidays, financial and legal information, entertainment, property, public and consumer information, recipes, the weather, sports results and games, etc., particularly if they have been accustomed to getting such information in other ways which they believe is less costly.

It is unwise to judge Prestel on the initial reaction to the first application, namely information retrieval. The more important consideration is that we now have an improved infrastructure with homes linked to computer centres, to businesses and to other homes and we need to explore how these improved links can be used with advantage. Already there are innovations with the introduction of a two-way message facility, closed user groups where access to certain data is restricted to only those in the group, a gateway system to enable data-bases in third party computers to be accessed, and further technical developments including improved graphics and 'picture Prestel'. The response facility enables requests for further information or the ordering of goods such as books, wine and theatre tickets paid for via a credit card number.

These developments illustrate the continuing search to exploit the new infrastructure in ways which are attractive to customers and commercially successful.

An important feature of the development of Prestel has been the number of organisations which have had to pool their talents for the service to get this far. The approach has been to establish the framework in a disciplined way with appropriate standards so that, for example, the suppliers of television sets could compete in providing sets adapted both for Prestel and the broadcasting services Ceefax and Oracle which are more suitable for accessing a much smaller data-base of fast-changing information.

Other key collaborators are the information providers. This raises a dilemma since ideally one would wish to encourage all comers to provide information in any way they preferred within the law, but the reputation of the service as a whole is affected by the general quality of the pages on offer and thus there is a contrary desire to 'manage' the quality and balance of the data-base to some extent.

At this early stage there is considerable scope for exploring how Prestel can be made more useful and investigating what factors deter the development of the domestic market. A trial of Prestel in 1979 in a U.K. Consumer Advice Centre involved staff who were all trained consumer advisers with good knowledge of traditional sources of information. They found that Prestel was particularly useful for information on consumer durable product price and service, on tourism, on comparative product/service testing, e.g. on used cars and on legal and Government data on such as retail food prices. They found they needed training on how to use Prestel effectively, e.g. to quickly obtain the right page, they should prepare their own index of more useful page numbers and they should have a general knowledge of what was available in the data-base.

It is an unsurprising conclusion that effort is needed to learn how to use a new tool, but having done so they were able to access certain types of information more quickly and more effectively than by previous methods. More recently a project has been launched by the Prestel Social Information Providers Group supported by the National Consumer Council and a Government grant. Prestel sets are being installed in Post Offices, Citizens Advice Bureaux, Social Security Offices and town halls in three experimental areas, to be used by the public with the help of trained staff. This will help identify how much difficulty the public has in using the system, the areas of most interest, etc. It is very important that such systems are used and are seen to be used on behalf of the general public to reduce the antipathy that would grow from private users having too much advantage, for example in job hunting, over those who did not have such good access to information gathering tools.

This account of the way the Prestel infrastructure is developing has touched upon a number of services in embryonic form: message services, home shopping, home banking and advertising in addition to the major applications of information services including elements of entertainment such as games.

However, other parts of the telecommunications network can be exploited to support these types of services and others such as telemetry and alarm services. For example, the packet switched data network can provide the basis for electronic funds transfer and retail applications which may become linked to the home. The computers which support this network can also be used to provide message services, and other computers and software are being introduced specifically to provide a comprehensive electronic mail service such as Telecom Gold's Dialcom Service and the Comet Service of British Leyland.

The next section will look at the residential market in these types of services before considering the network features required to support them.

Service Prospects

a. *Information Services*

The attraction of a service like Prestel is that the consumer goes more directly to what is wanted and only receives the information requested and hence accesses the information more rapidly. The updating facilities keep the information as current as it needs to be and it is available 24 hours a day, seven days a week. The page format puts a premium on concise and effective presentation.

Our studies of the demand for information services in the home and the extent to which they are satisfied by existing media show that there are different needs for direct search, for study and for browsing and one must distinguish between normal and exceptional circumstances, for example, what to do following a death in the family. The areas where a new medium such as Prestel are most useful are directed search, particularly where the local information provision is poor, for such items as legal advice and repair services; when information is needed in a hurry or at inconvenient times; and when one needs advice on where to find more detailed information. The need for extended information is more acute for big decisions like buying a house or planning a vacation. Accessibility, familiarity and ease of use determine which sources and media are used, which makes it difficult for a new medium to get established.

Consumers are not a homogeneous mass. Many prefer verbal interaction face to face or over a telephone to gather information, for social reasons or because of difficulties in comprehending written material. However, perhaps the most influential consumers are the elite group of information seekers who tend to subscribe to *Which?* and have a disproportionate influence over supplier product policies. They are likely to be more thorough in their information searching and to explore the effectiveness of new media. Another impetus to the provision of information services comes from the information supplier finding them a more effective medium for promulgating information, whether it be a non-commercial organisation passing on a public service message or a commercial organisation improving the information content of commercial messages. However, until the service is well established the effectiveness is blunted by the small number of customers currently able to receive the message.

b. Entertainment

The United Kingdom is rightly proud of its broadcasting traditions which have combined quality and diversity. New offerings are being planned with Channel 4 and breakfast television in the offing, and satellite broadcasting has now been approved initially for two channels to be offered by the BBC. Hence there is a lot of new entertainment in the pipeline.

In the United States the pattern of development has been different. The commercial networks have been accused in the past of being so influenced by viewing ratings that originality and diversity was stifled with a convergence on the most popular type of programming. Partly as an escape from the dissatisfaction with the main networks, local cable television networks were introduced offering such attractions as more recent movies. The growth of such networks was unspectacular until the quality and diversity of programming available over the cable networks improved substantially through the capacity to distribute material via satellite. This changed the economics of the systems and opened up the possibility of a wider range of interests being served including minority groups (ethnic or special interest), more local programming, and spectaculars. The result is that cable is now growing more rapidly (although still well short of half the population), but there is continuing controversy about the possible impact on the broadcasting networks. For example, concern is expressed that the cable networks might outbid the networks for, say, major sporting events and have the effect of reducing the quality of what is available to all for the benefit of the fewer number of cable subscribers.

Some would argue that there is less need for cable systems in the U.K. where we have been well served by broadcast services in the past and our disposable income is less than in the U.S.A. However, on average we spend 20 hours per week in front of the television set, the existing Pay TV trials have been reasonably well supported despite some restrictions and the video cassette recorder market is doing well despite charges of £15 per month. Hence there seems to be market

potential for new entertainment services which knowledgeable observers think will flourish if the market is allowed to develop. Nevertheless
the impact this might have on the quality and economics of broadcasting services generally is likely to be fiercely debated in the coming
months.

Other forms of entertainment including hi fi stereophonic audio,
electronic games and selections from video libraries are also potentially
attractive. Video techniques exploiting movement and colour could
first be developed for entertainment but have relevance also to
information services and education.

c. Education

Education is closely linked to entertainment and information
services. In certain instances the receiver needs to act on the basis of
the information received; in others, the information consumption is an
end in itself. This affects the technical capability that is needed. Cable,
videocassettes and discs are likely to be suitable for educational
applications. In some cases video will be significant, for example in car
maintenance, and interactive media are particularly appropriate
allowing the student to repeat or skip material as required. Educational
materials for self improvement and the learning of special skills are two
of the most popular items in the U.S. with demand for more formal
high school, college and adult education courses only slightly less.

The extent to which educational applications grow will depend very
much on whether organisations develop materials targetted at the
home market alongside services to the formal education sector. The
Open University will have an influential role to play here since it is
accustomed to exploiting new technology and to dealing with home
based students.

d. Home Shopping

For many people shopping has a social value and they certainly want
to see items such as perishable goods and second hand cars before they
buy. Hence although it may be possible to inspect still or moving
pictures of products and to enter orders from home, they would not be

very interested in such a service. However, single people in full time employment and two income families may find such a service convenient. It can also reduce the search time and effort even if the final choice is made after inspection. The organisations most likely to be interested are mail order and direct selling companies. There are about 100 million mail order transactions per year mainly to social categories C–E while direct selling is mainly to categories A–B facilitated by the use of credit cards.

The result is that home shopping is likely to develop slowly with initial sales of products such as wine and airline tickets based on written descriptions alone. Video presentations are likely to become economic at higher penetrations and hence are less likely for some time to come.

e. Advertising

The impact of new services on advertising revenue is extremely important for the economics of current and new services but is difficult to predict at this stage. It seems plausible that if new services such as broadcasting to minority groups were introduced they could generate new advertising attracted by the more specific targetting of their message. This may not displace advertising in other places. However, it seems equally plausible that with more outlets for advertising revenue the total spent may not grow proportionately and there could then be less for each contender than before. More specifically there could in the long run be a switch of advertisements from newspapers to videotext systems if that became a more effective way of selling goods. This might have a similar effect to the growth in the use of cars on local public transport, where the choice of others influences the services available to the individual who might still prefer what he had in the past.

f. Telemetry

The public utilities would benefit in two ways with the reduction in cost of meter readings and better control over consumption. This is possible over the existing telecommunications network, and British

Telecom and the South Eastern Electricity Board are collaborating on a field trial. The consumer will no doubt share in the benefits. The trend here is towards the remote control of devices in the home using the telephone network. This will complement the increasing tendency for home products to be programmable to preset instructions.

g. Alarm and Security Services

This is a bigger market in the U.S.A. partly because of higher crime rates, and U.K. insurance companies at present do not give premium reductions to protected residential premises. Small businesses are important in this market. There are substantial prospects for social service applications such as monitoring the activity of the elderly to detect whether the lack of movement suggests something is amiss.

Surveillance applications often require video capability, which in most cases can be satisfactorily supported by the telecommunications network with cable eventually providing scope for improvements in quality.

h. Home Banking

The majority of people do not have bank accounts hence the opportunities are restricted in the short term. Mention has already been made of the potential use of credit cards. The most likely applications for home banking are in making remote payments for regular bills, requesting bank statements on demand and the capability to update standing orders from home.

i. Message Services

Reference has also been made to electronic mail from home but the residential market for messages is much smaller than the business market.

Technical Options

All of the services listed above with the exception of entertainment are capable of being offered over the telecommunications network. It is arguable whether the speed and quality of a visual picture from Picture Prestel, for example, would be adequate for teleshopping applications. For some it will be, for others it will not.

However, in the near future it is clear that the new service that could be economically viable on its own is entertainment television, offered over cable networks. There is a number of technical options for cable systems. The most significant characteristic is the extent to which 'return path' is possible, i.e. the subscriber can send information back as well as receiving it, which has a major effect on the services available over the system. The simplest and cheapest system would have a basic coax tree topology which could support broadcasting services, teletext services (akin to Ceefax and Oracle) and FM radio retransmission.

A one-way addressable system would allow additional features such as parental discretion coding, pay per view for special events booked in advance and one-way information services and text advertisements. An interactive two-way system would support impulse pay per view and the services quoted in the last section to varying degrees while a multistar system would provide improved video capability for such services as teleshopping, video library services and more than one television channel per household.

Ninety per cent of the systems in the U.S.A. are of the one-way variety but the new systems being built are all two-way. If Britain goes ahead with cable television, it needs to adopt technology which can evolve from the initial emphasis on entertainment services into the other types of service listed which in the longer term are expected to become more significant. However, if the simpler systems are introduced, these additional services will need to wait for the replacement of such networks, which would delay them for decades.

If cable systems are established before the introduction of direct broadcasting satellite transmissions in 1986 then it would benefit both cable and DBS to distribute DBS via a community antenna and the cable system, as well as direct to roof top antennas in non-cabled districts. Cable distribution may also be preferred on environmental grounds. In this way DBS and cable may be complementary in some areas and at the same time compete to get established in others. Most of the non-entertainment services require a return path which would need to be via the telecommunications network in areas where DBS antenna penetration precluded the introduction of cable.

Video-discs and video-cassettes are in competition for residential expenditure with cable and DBS but are complementary in, for example, educational applications and coping with programme clashes which is more likely with greater diversity.

Other technical developments will also help in the mid to late eighties such as high definition television and digital colour television receivers with a full frame store which will be an important asset for video display for information and teleshopping services. It would be too costly for these services or others such as video library selection to take up a wideband link for an extended period of time.

Some National Policy Considerations

In the last section it was suggested that for the U.K. to develop a broadband framework which would support a full range of services it should avoid introducing the more basic technology which only caters for broadcasting service or even one-way services. The costs to cable the more promising parts of the country are likely to be at least £3 billion and could be £10 billion depending on how wide these were spread. This is a significant element of national investment whether the funds come from private or public sources. Even if private investors were willing to put in the required amounts it does not follow that all the activities must then be undertaken by the private sector. One must exploit the expertise that is available wherever it exists—some in the private sector, some in the public sector.

Although there may be some preoccupation with the broadcasting issues in the short term, it would be a mistake if the franchise and regulatory arrangements for cable were dominated by these considerations. We must look ahead to the emergence of a nationwide broadband system, with many applications on an area basis but others countrywide, such as widespread access to a first night or the successor to a mail order firm whose customers are nationwide. This requires the development of a disciplined infrastructure with appropriate attention to standards but with maximum scope for competition and diversity of use of the infrastructure. British Telecom was a key force in developing the framework in the Prestel case which provided competitive opportunities for set manufacturers and information providers and would be strongly placed to play a similar major role in creating a cable network infrastructure, which should be exploited by a wide range of programme and information service providers.

Two particular features of communications policy are the supreme importance of standards to enable interconnections from any source to any destination and the difficulty in building up a communications service where the value is dependent on the number of subscribers (the value of the telephone service to the initial subscribers must have been very questionable). Experience suggests that standards are introduced more readily by a dominant force influenced by others than through a committee. The second consideration suggests a lengthy period of build-up before such services reach profitability, and hence one needs to have a lengthy period in mind for recovery of one's investment.

Residential—Business Links

Residential and business considerations cannot be completely separated for several reasons. Firstly the efforts to find out how information technology can help individuals are initially concentrated in the business environment. For example, research into the so called 'Office of the Future' is not about improving typical office functions such as typing and filing which would make a very limited contribution to the effectiveness of an organisation. It is more a question of finding out how various levels in a business administer their affairs in the broadest sense including information gathering and dissemination, holding meetings and decision making, and how information technology can improve performance.

For example, there are useful features which can be added to a telephone to ease the setting up of calls such as short code dialling, to re-route or establish conference calls with more than one party or to monitor the cost of a call. However, these additional features do not deal with two major irritations about the telephone—the unavailability of the called person and the intrusive nature of the 'phone whose ring only a strong minded individual can ignore. These will be dealt with by the development during the 1980s of more sophisticated voice services so that a caller can store his voice message and the called party who was not available for whatever reason can retrieve the message when it is convenient to do so and transfer it in its original form to others if appropriate. The application will be even more useful when you can insert or retrieve calls remotely. Equivalent systems for text messages are currently available.

Many of these improvements will be developed first in the business environment but are also relevant to the residential customer.

Secondly, the prices at which services can be offered are often dependent on customer volume, and success in the business market can be crucial to reducing the price to a level attractive in the residential market.

Thirdly, developments in information technology will support more distributed organisational structures and allow more people to work locally or at home should they wish to do so. Neighbourhood work centres could emerge with communications facilities which exceed what each firm could afford on its own. Many recoil at the concept of working from home as socially undesirable but in the U.S.A. home terminals are enabling husband and wife to continue to work but sharing the baby minding, with mother at home three days a week and father two days. This illustrates that the technology can increase the choices open even though many may still favour the traditional choice.

Problems

It is not possible to introduce a new medium without generating some problems, real or imagined, although there seems to be more realisation than in days gone by of the need to anticipate these or deal with them at an early stage.

In the case of videotext systems, for example, it is difficult to provide a service cheaply at the early stage of development or to provide an efficient and effective user friendly system for the ordinary consumer who is not accustomed to interacting with technical systems. There is a basic problem of the labelling of the message—distinguishing between advertising and objective information. There could be difficulty with payment arrangements when the information is so ephemeral. It may be possible for major information providers to use their powerful position to monopolise the information on certain goods or to use the information facilities to develop cartels. However they have similar power in the use of other media and one might argue that smaller firms are more likely to compete via the new medium than they would through traditional media. There is also a basic problem of responsibility for the content of the data in the data-base. Clearly it is appropriate for the suppliers of information to take responsibility for the content but that still leaves some doubt about how the public should be protected from being duped by an unscrupulous provider.

Some more general themes have been alluded to such as the effect of the competition for advertising revenue, the possible increase in the information gap between the 'haves' and the 'have nots' and the impact on regional policy where for example cable developments could be positive but competition policy in communications be negative by reinforcing existing industrial activity patterns.

However, there is always a reaction against innovation and while it is wise to be on the alert for problems it is not appropriate to become too constrained at an early stage by envisaging difficulties that in theory might arise, when there is little practical evidence to date.

Concluding Remarks

The kinds of mass communication services discussed in this chapter are at an early stage of development. Service providers and customers need to adapt to electronic alternatives to existing services, and new uses will be developed with experience, e.g. professionals such as lawyers may present their services in new ways which are a departure from past practices.

There is much we need to learn about behavioural characteristics, what user friendliness means to different consumers, and the significance of colour, movement or visual images to conveying information. Consumers may have sharply different preferences for new services. The influential ones need to be differentiated. So do the applications that appeal to a wide audience.

The U.S.A. is ahead of the U.K. in experience of cable systems and behind in videotext systems, and overall the level of knowledge about the applications in this chapter is about the same.

A full range of new services including video applications will appear much earlier if far sighted decisions are made in the technology for cable television systems, although some video and most of the other applications can also be provided over telecommunications networks.

With the exception of entertainment services most of the new services will be developed first for the business environment.

The rate of take up of many services is likely to be sluggish in the early years but accelerate when a critical mass is reached or they can ride on the back of other services which have made the breakthrough.

9

Social and Employment Implications of Information Technology

PAUL WILLMAN

Department of Social and Economic Studies, Imperial College

Introduction

Economists and sociologists have been in more or less continuous discussion about the social implications of technological change for at least the last three decades. The 'automation debate' of the 1950s and 1960s aroused considerable concern about the future of employment and the nature of work, perhaps more so in the U.S.A. than in the U.K. From one perspective, then, the debate on the social impact of information technology related to just one more step in a process of continuous technical change which must be of interest to the social scientist, or policy maker.

However, others, who perhaps take a pessimistic view about the future performance of western economies, see a quantum difference between technological changes of the recent past and those which are here or are impending. From this perspective, "economic information technology represents (a) 'heartland' technology critical for our entire future",[1] which will impact both on industry and services in the development of distinctively new processes and products. Information technology thus presents policy makers with intractable problems. If it is a heartland technology, then clearly there is no alternative to rapid uptake in order to maintain competitive performance both at home and abroad. However, such rapid adoption may accelerate a recessionary phase of labour displacement producing severe frictional problems in the short to medium term. Both socially and politically, these problems may be unacceptable.

A second set of concerns relate to the nature of work. There is by now a considerable body of literature which argues that 'degradation' or de-skilling of work is an inevitable consequence of technological advances.[2] It is argued that information technology will affect the 'middle range' of skills — office work and crafts included — in such a way as to generate a socially undesirable polarisation of the workforce into the highly skilled and thus marketable and the completely unskilled. Whether this rather extreme view is true or not, there will clearly be considerable changes in certain jobs as a consequence of technological change which will cause at least short run problems for government and industry.

It is essential, therefore, to examine both the means by which innovation may be encouraged and such consequences allowed for; this implies a concern with three broad areas. The first and most general is the concern with the employment consequences of information technology; secondly, the factors influencing the decisions of companies to innovate and the form of organisation they adopt to cope with it; thirdly, the industrial relations consequences of change. This short paper will deal with each in turn.

Employment Aspects

There is no lack of employment forecasts predicting the dire consequences of the adoption of information technology on overall levels of employment. Such studies have resurrected the spectre of technological employment: that is, unemployment associated with output per head rising faster than total output.[3] The generation of this employment is seen to lie in the pervasive nature of information technology. Previously, it is argued, employment has tended to move from primary industries, to manufacturing to services, as economies developed. Now, it is precisely those service industries which have in the past absorbed the labour displaced from extracting and manufacturing industries which will fall victim to technological change. An ASTMS document summarises 'occupations at risk' as constituting 62 per cent of all occupations while Robinson calculates the 'information sector' to which labour-saving technology will be applied at about 50 per cent of the workforce; estimates of unemployment levels above five million are being presented.[4]

A number of points need to be made here. The first has been hinted at already: against the dire prophecies of job loss following technological change need to be set the employment consequences of *not* innovating. The expansion of output which would sustain employment where labour productivity rises is more likely to be achieved by those companies or nations which innovate most rapidly and effectively, than by those which lag behind in terms of price or product performance.

Secondly, the U.K. economy is already experiencing high unemployment, for reasons other than a rapid rate of technological change. The slow growth of the world economy, demographic trends which will increase the size of the workforce over the next ten years, a large percentage of declining industries and a weak competitive position will all generate employment problems in the U.K. throughout the 1980s in the view of a number of economic forecasts.[5] Those industries such as textiles, road transport and steel which have shed large amounts of labour recently, have not done so primarily as a consequence of indigenous technological change. Rather, several have been subject to foreign competition from countries where such changes have taken place.

In fact, innovating industries may generate employment in a number of ways. The increased returns from innovation may increase investment in new processes, albeit with a lower labour content. Alternatively, such firms may reduce prices, allowing for an expansion of demand. Finally, trade unions in innovating sectors may succeed in increasing wage rates, allowing increases in demand and employment.

Thirdly, it is generally easier to identify information technology-based processes which are likely to be both pervasive and labour saving — such as photocomposition in newspapers, electronic switching in telecommunications, robotic assembly in vehicles — than new products or services which may generate demand for labour. This is because in comparison to the time-scale of process innovation, the

generation of employment by expansion of output or product development is relatively long term. Enormously expensive studies, such as
that by the Arthur Little Company, attempt assessments of net job
creation on a global scale — and indeed the results at that time were
not grounds for optimism.[6] However, such exercises are basically
sophisticated guesswork, particularly concerning the important question of *where* such newly developed industries will be sited.

One necessary distinction here is between actual and perceived job
loss. The paragraphs above indicate that a reliable estimate of actual
net employment gain or loss in consequence of information technology
is almost impossible to achieve. Those effects are clearly important in
terms of national planning, but other considerations are crucial.
Perceived effects will, however, influence the climate of opinion within
companies on information technology. For example, in some cases job
losses are seen straightforwardly to follow from technological change,
as in Fleet Street.[7] However, work at Imperial College indicates that
the effects of change are not generally viewed in this way: even in firms
which shed labour while innovating, it is frequently the case that
process innovation is seen as the basis of arresting such decline.[8]

In assessing the impact of information technology, therefore, it is
important to look at particular industries and companies, and indeed
at particular uses of information technology. It is after all, rather
simplistic to assume that computer aided design, computer numerical
control, word processing and automatic banking will all have the same
unidirectional impact on employment levels in different companies,
just as it is too simple to assume that product development and output
expansion — both sensitive to external economic conditions in any
event — will fail to compensate. One must look in detail at behaviour
in particular companies.

Impact on Industrial Organisation

Within organisations, there are at least three sets of concerns. The first
set surrounds the decision to innovate. Companies may see the need for
innovation as lying in a number of areas — product design, labour
costs, capacity — and the rate of innovation will follow accordingly.
Secondly, the adaptation the organisation makes to cope with changed

processes, and thirdly, the manpower requirements and policies which emerge after change. I shall deal with each in turn.

1. *Decision on innovation*

A recent P.S.I. survey of 1200 manufacturing establishments in Britain[9] discovered that just over half of the establishments were not using or planning to use microelectronics in processes or in products: this represented about 45 per cent of total manufacturing employment. Over half of these realised that there was scope for microprocessor applications, but were still not planning to do anything about it. These findings raise a number of general questions about the constraints on innovation in British industry.

Currently, there are at least three general theories of company innovation behaviour. Neo-classical economic theory of the firm implies that companies engage in expensive market search for information on product market opportunities and technical process developments, innovating in process or product only to maximise profitability. The implications of this view are firstly, a detailed knowledge of available technology and secondly, that systematic costings of innovation will be attempted.

The neo-classical view has been modified by behaviouralists, such as Simon,[10] who argue that firms only search for alternatives when they encounter a problem, and this limited search activity ceases when a satisfactory, not necessarily optimal, solution is found. This implies a much lower level of knowledge of the product and process market.

Thirdly, a radical view suggests that the purpose of innovation is to maintain a tighter control over the labour force.[11] This implies that production processes will be developed to reduce the overall labour requirement, fragment jobs and allow close monitoring of market performance.

Because of the relatively low rate of uptake of information technology in the U.K. it is difficult to decide which of these theories is most accurate. Clearly, both the first and third are slightly implausible. Many British companies do not appear to maintain technological awareness on the basis of extensive market search. The idea that in the present economic climate companies which engage in large capital investment in information technology will do so on strictly financial grounds is unsound. Particularly where information technology is allied to expensive machinery as in CNC, it will frequently be extremely difficult to demonstrate conclusively the advantage of new rather than labour-intensive conventional technology since the return on investment will be extremely sensitive to the level of capacity utilisation.

The radical approach is also implausible. It may be the case that particular companies experience severe problems with an intransigent labour force, and so seek labour-displacing technology; one could cull examples from Fleet Street, from the Italian motor industry,[12] or, less emotively, from companies suffering high secretarial turnover in the London area. All might innovate to solve this basic problem. However, it is unlikely to be a more general difficulty as against competitive pressures in the product market, particularly for those industries with low labour costs and good industrial relations.

It is thus the problem-centred approach which seems most plausible: firms will consider information technology as one possible solution to competitive or other difficulties. Design changes may require components which cannot be handled by conventional technology. Delivery times may be uncompetitive. Old machinery may wear out and require replacement. Competitors may display flexibility in the provision of services which cannot be easily imitated. In all of these cases, information technology is not the only solution. The choice of innovation as a response depends on a number of factors.

Two stimuli appear particularly important from the findings of the Imperial College Project. Firstly, the existence of government grants specifically for microelectronics technology applications stimulated activity in several plants. More frequently companies benefited from the presence of an 'innovation champion' somewhere within the organisation, pushing changes through.[13] Obviously, a policy for sponsoring innovation could provide the former but could hardly rely on the latter: such a policy would need perhaps to consider removing the *obstacles* to innovation.

These obstacles vary across industrial sectors. Perhaps the principal one is the availability of capital for projects which may not definitely yield returns. In the British car industry, for example, public funding of relatively high risk operations was crucial for the adoption of robotic welding at BL. In the mechanical engineering industry, the presence of large numbers of small firms, and a number of multiplant enterprises which have not rationalised pre-merger structures, means that few companies are able to field a large manufacturing engineering effort to develop in-house new technology applications. External purchase is thus necessary, but historically low profit margins mean that funds for such purchase are frequently unavailable.

In other industries, different sets of constraints operate. In banking, for example, EDP systems are widely used. On-line data transmission, electronic funds transfer and computer-based credit and debit information are increasingly common. Given the profitability of the sector, the availability of in-house DP expertise, the lack of substantial worker resistance and the returns on the use of information technology, one would expect this. However, competitive pressures have served to slow down the rate at which change is adopted, particularly at the customer interface in the installation of autotellers. In the U.K., relatively low numbers of dispensers had been adopted by 1980, principally due to the need to overcome customer resistance.[14] Similar constraints in the form of a retained commitment to item pricing have hindered the adoption of scanners in the U.S. food retailing sector.[15]

The second obstacle is management expertise. Senker and Swords-Isherwood, in a comparative study of the U.K. and Germany, found higher management resistance to the adoption of CNC in the U.K. Line managers may need considerable persuasion and education to make use of new technology, and to develop the necessary new technical and managerial skills.[16] For example, under conventional technology within manufacturing industry, production managers in the past may have been concerned with the maintenance of labour productivity, reducing absenteeism and turnover, and supervising work and bonuses. With new technology, the manager needs less man management skills, and greater ability to cope with a complex interrelationship of networks within and between departments. This interdependence is increased by faster throughput of materials and product and because more complex machines require more support functions.[17]

2. Organisational adaptations

The first issue here is the impact of information technology on organisational structure. Information technology obviously facilitates the collection, transmission and collation of data. Some argue, therefore that innovation will have a centralising effect, as the cost of getting accurate information to head offices is reduced. Others argue that increased ease of monitoring will mean that decisions previously taken at the centre, because those at the periphery could not be trusted, can now be decentralised but monitored. The latter view is supported by the correlation observed in bureaucratic organisations between the degree of bureaucratisation and decentralisation.[18]

Michael Earl, for example, argues that information technology will accelerate devolutionary trends: by encouraging the use of micro-computers locally for irregular tasks as 'slack resources', by permitting the development of specialist functions, and by facilitating the development of functionally-based information systems.[19]

Less equivocal perhaps is the impact of information technology on the complexity of organisations. Galbraith takes the view that organisations are basically information processing systems, and suggests that, as the amount of information to be processed increases, then the requisite organisational structure shifts to matrix form, with integrating functions to handle the complexity. This implies some difficulties for organisations seeking rapid adaptation to thoroughgoing innovation.

3. Manpower requirements

It is clearly easy to list the sorts of jobs which, in one view, will suffer from the implementation of information technology: robotics requires less assembly workers, computer-aided design less draughtsmen, office automation systems fewer clerks, all at given levels of output. However, different views of the context and consequences of office automation exist. Driscoll, for example, clearly sees such automation as a kind of blanket phenomenon inducing similar changes in a range of organisations, resulting in a highly skilled powerful elite directing the operations of ranks of unskilled clerks.[20] However, for Hammer and Sirbu, who define office automation rather crucially as "the utilization of technology to *improve* the realization of office functions", the occupational distribution implied is rather different. In such an environment "office workers become more like craftsmen rather than assembly line workers ... the great majority of office workers will enjoy greater autonomy and responsibility than they currently do".[21]

In any event, other skills will be in greater demand. Many are predicting massive shortfalls in supply of computer programmers in the U.K. over the next 10 years. In an economy crucially short of certain engineering craft skills,[22] against a backdrop of declining employment numbers,[23] the development of dual craftsmen with a combination of electrical and mechanical skills will be difficult. Some employers, such as ICI and BL, have had reasonably well-publicised problems with the training of such staff: but others have had similar experiences.[24]

In an economy so obviously prone to crucial skill shortages as in the U.K., the training and retraining of labour is vital. At a time when the Industrial Training Boards are being cut, when certain long-standing deficiencies in the education of British engineers have been pointed out[25] and when Training Opportunities Programme qualifications are not always well considered in job applications, it could be argued that the correct economic measures to develop the necessary human capital are not being undertaken wholeheartedly. This is in fact the argument of the TUC, who have a great deal to say about technological change.

4. Industrial relations issues

The TUC in Britain has consistently developed policies on technological change over the past 30 years or so. Successive documents in 1956 and 1965 on 'Automation and Technological Change' exhibited a general approach which has re-emerged recently in policy statements on information technology.[26] Over the past three years, member trade unions have exhibited in their publications and policy statements considerable awareness of both the potentialities and threats of 'new technology', as well as manifesting a concern that such technologies be adopted as quickly as possible to improve the competitive position of British industry.

With few exceptions, such statements emphasise the inevitability of technical change before outlining measures to deal with it.[27] The most comprehensive and influential statement is that of the TUC itself, which incorporated a set of economic policy proposals squarely within the tripartite traditions of the Social Contract era, combined with a rather adventurous set of collective bargaining goals.[28] The latter are of greater interest for two reasons: firstly, the economic policy goals largely recapitulate themes and demands familiar to readers of the TUC Economic Review over the past ten years; secondly, such goals are currently less influential than formerly, and, generally, the approach favoured by the TUC has gone by the board.

The presentation of a systematic agenda for bargaining over information technology revealed the considerable development of the TUC's thinking in this area since the automation debates in the 1950s. The checklist is presented opposite: the key feature is that, apart from a more 'traditional' set of job security devices which add to or reinforce statutory employee rights, there is a desire to extend collective bargaining to areas traditionally regarded as lying within managerial prerogative. The TUC have proposed the extension of trade union influence over all stages of the implementation procedure: documents of member unions echo this concern.[29]

However, employers do not wholly agree. Although this approach was endorsed by the TUC Congress of 1979, and a version of a joint statement recommended by CBI Council to its membership, the CBI members themselves were unwilling to consider such an extension of influence.[30] In addition, the success of member unions in negotiating the extension of bargaining over information technology since then has been limited. Comparatively few technology agreements have been signed, and there is by now some evidence to indicate that this does not simply reflect the absence of innovation by companies.[31]

In BL, for example, the development of the Metro works was not accompanied by collective bargaining even though a well developed participation scheme had operated in the past. In the banking industry, technological developments have proceeded apace, without B.I.F.U. (the banking union) being able to implement their policies for the control of technological change. Many of the agreements which do exist cover predominantly white collar workers: for example, the agreement on extension of computers in Ford, and the recently signed interim agreement on the introduction of new technology in the Civil Service.[32] There are several reasons for this.

TUC CHECKLIST

1. Change must be by agreement: consultation with trade unions should begin prior to the decision to purchase, and *status quo* provisions should operate until agreement is reached.
2. Machinery must be developed to cope with technical change which emphasises the central importance of collective bargaining.
3. Information relevant to decision making should be made available to union representatives or nominees prior to any decision being taken.
4. There must be agreement both on employment and output levels within the company. Guarantees of job security, redeployment and relocation agreements must be achieved. In addition, enterprises should be committed to an expansion of output after technical change.
5. Company retraining commitments must be stepped up, with priority for those affected by new technology. Earnings levels must be secured.
6. The working week should be reduced to 35 hours, systematic overtime should be eliminated and shift patterns altered.
7. The benefits of new technology must be distributed. Innovation must occasion improvements in terms and conditions of service.
8. Negotiators should seek influence over the design of equipment, and in particular should seek to control work or performance measurement through the new technology.
9. Stringent health and safety standards must be observed.
10. Procedures for reviewing progress, and study teams on the new technology should be established.

From: *Employment and Technology.*

First, the negotiation of technological change in this way requires a considerable amount of knowledge of information technology: it is much more likely that white collar unions — organising computer staff, designers and perhaps engineers — will be able to call upon such expertise. In some manual unions, it might simply be the case that input to the design and implementation process is not possible without expensive resort to outside consultants.

The likelihood of this resort is diminished by the tendency of many manual unions to negotiate on a plant-by-plant basis, even within multi-plant companies.[33] Under such bargaining arrangements, the use of consultants becomes inordinately expensive. Moreover, since innovation tends to be at least company or industry wide, plant level bargaining may be in any event wholly inappropriate as a means for discussing such change. Bargaining reform thus becomes a prerequisite for the extension of bargaining, but such reform is difficult to achieve in the typical case where several unions bargain in concert. The typically British tendency towards multi-unionism may prevent the negotiation of change.

Even where bargaining structures facilitate negotiated change, bargaining styles may prevent it. For example, many British unions are well established in the tradition of bargaining change for cash, and have been encouraged in this tendency by a decade of incomes policies allowing exceptions for productivity deals. Such deals may raise the costs of change for employers. In other instances, trade unions may be unable to accept change because of its implications for their membership base. The classic case here is in the national newspaper industry, and the reaction of the National Graphical Association to the introduction of photocomposition: the typical union response is a more or less thoroughgoing unwillingness to cooperate in the context of a deficiency of technical expertise on the management side.[34] These aggressive styles of bargaining tend to be more entrenched among craft trade unions.

Finally, white collar unions are more likely to seek technology agreements because — as indicated above — many basically simple clerical tasks are prone to change by the adoption of information technology. Most unions in the Civil Service, APEX in the private sector, TASS in draughting jobs and the Communication Workers

Union in the Post Office have many members in such jobs. Information technology may thus be seen as an issue of organisational survival for the union concerned, and policy development will proceed accordingly.

One of the central concerns of many participants and observers is the capacity of the British industrial relations system to adopt to rapid technological change. It is often argued that British unions are obstructive or exact too high a price for the acceptance of technological change. The policy commitments of many unions are prefaced by the concern to promote technological change, although even the General Council are pessimistic about the commitment of rank and file trade unionists.[35] However, research at Imperial College into microprocessor-based process innovations in manufacturing industry does not indicate that protracted negotiations slow down the rate of technological advance. It appears that many trade unionists recognise the necessity of information technology within their enterprises, and react accordingly.[36]

Conclusion

In summary, then, it seems clear that an acceleration of the rate of uptake of information technology in all sectors — manufacturing, services, public and private sector — is essential if the generally weak competitive position of the U.K. economy is to be remedied. For the policy-maker, and for the social scientist, the central problem is something of a paradox: how to remove the undoubted institutional obstacles to rapid change while simultaneously taking steps to ensure that the short-term social costs are not unnecessarily high. The appropriate measures for resolving this paradox — market mechanisms or directive planning — remain the subject of political debate. But clearly, some solution must be found.

References

1. C. Freeman, *Unemployment and Government*, J.D. Bernal Memorial Lecture, Birkbeck College, London, May 1978.
2. J.R. Bright, "The Relationship of Increasing Automation and Skill Requirements", in (eds) National Committee on Technology, Automation and Economic Progress,

The Employment Impact of Technological Change, Washington D.C. 1966; H. Braverman *Labour and Monopoly Capital,* Monthly Review Press 1974.

3. European Trade Union Institute *The Impact of Microelectronics on Employment in Western Europe in the 1980s,* Brussels 1980.

4. Association of Scientific and Managerial Staffs *Technological Change and Collective Bargaining,* London 1979; C. Jenkins and B. Sherman *The Collapse of Work,* Eyre Methuen 1979.

5. Cambridge Economic Policy Group, *Economic Policy Review 1979 and 1980.*

6. Arthur D. Little Associates. *Strategic Impact of Intelligent Electronics in US and Western Europe,* 1979.

7. R. Martin, *Technological Change and Industrial Relations in Fleet Street,* Oxford 1981.

8. A. Francis, M. Snell, P. Willman and G. Winch, *The Impact of Information Technology at Work: The Case of CAD/CAM and MIS in Engineering Plants,* Imperial College 1981. Forthcoming.

9. J. Northcott, P. Rogers and A. Zeilinger, *Microelectronics in Industry, Extent of Use,* Policy Studies Institute, London 1981.

10. H.A. Simon, 'A Behavioural Model of Rational Choice', *Quarterly Journal of Economics,* Vol. 69, pp. 99–118, 1955.

11. e.g. Braverman *op. cit.*

12. Martin *op. cit.*

13. Francis *et al op. cit.*

14. F.I.E.T. *Bank Workers and the New Technology,* Geneva 1980.

15. United Food and Commercial Workers, *Item Pricing,* Washington, D.C. 1980.

16. N. Swords-Isherwood and P. Senker, 'Management Resistance to the New Technology', in T. Forester (ed.), *The Microelectronics Revolution,* Basil Blackwell, Oxford, 198, pp. 408–14,.

17. Francis *et al. op. cit.*

18. J. Child, 'Organisational Structure and Strategies of Control', *Administrative Science Quarterly,* 1972.

19. M. Earl, 'What Micros mean for Managers', in Forester, *op. cit.,* pp. 356–67.

20. J.Driscoll, *How to Humanize Office Automation,* M.I.T. 1980.

21. H. Hammer and M. Sirbu *What is Office Automation,* M.I.T. 1980.

22. National Economic Development Office, *Engineering Craftsmen: Shortages and Related Problems,* N.E.D.O., London 1977.

23. Swords-Isherwood and Senker, *op. cit.*

24. G. Bamber 'Microchips and Industrial Relations', *Industrial Relations Journal* 1980.

25. Finneston Report, *Engineering Our Future,* H.M.S.O. 1980.

26. T.U.C. *Automation and Technical Change,* Congress House 1956 and 1965.

27. e.g. APEX, *Office Automation,* London, 1979.

28. T.U.C. *Employment and Technology,* Congress House. 1979.

29. e.g. Banking, Insurance and Finance Union.

30. See *Industrial Relations Review and Report,* No. 232, September 1980.

31. R. Mosely and R. Williams, *Trade Unions and New Technology: An Overview of Technology Agreements,* Technology Policy Unit 1981.

32. *Financial Times* 18.3.81.

33. W. Brown (ed.), *The Changing Contours of Collective Bargaining in Great Britain,* Blackwell 1981.

34. Martin, *op. cit.*

35. T.U.C. *Economic Review,* p. 23, 1979.

36. Francis *et al. op. cit.*

10

Information Technology and Education

ROBIN CHAMBERS
Headteacher, Stoke Newington School, London

I SUSPECT that when most people refer to "the pressing need to introduce information technology (IT) into schools, technical colleges and universities", what they have in mind is the need to make available to "our brightest and best" the IT essential for success in the world of tomorrow — or indeed in the world of later on today. They are thinking of the "future generations of professionals" who must be able to compete with the highest fliers of other countries "such as Japan", where "the process of introducing IT into schools is already well advanced..."

All of which is fair comment, and undeniable, and self-evidently desirable. However, if that was all there was to it I for one would be deeply disappointed. There is much, much more to it than that. For the first time since the idea of schooling for all was conceived we have the means to make schools places of effective, successful learning for *all* children; and surely anyone who has ever been to school, and certainly anyone who has ever taught in an inner city comprehensive school, must realise what an epoch-making advance *that* would be.

In the first of the BBC programmes on computers and computer-assisted learning, the presenter stood in the middle of Stonehenge, which he described as an early kind of computer, programmed to tell the passing of the seasons by the movement of the stars. He told us that modern computers could gather meteorological data from all over the globe and in four hours predict the weather in any part of the world. "Even if I had been able to collect the data for a single day", I think he went on, "to make the calculations by hand I would have had to have begun before Stonehenge was built."

It is *that* kind of qualitative difference in education which we are talking about: not merely doing things more quickly and therefore more efficiently than before; but for the first time being able to do things which before we could hardly even begin to do. We did not have the resources before; and now they are within our grasp.

First, let us be clear what we mean by 'Education'. It is important at least to sketch in the parameters. Views differ. How often does one hear it said that schools have got their heads buried in the sand? "Schools have lost touch with the real world", people say; "the curriculum is irrelevant to today's needs". And what about tomorrow's challenges? There should be more science, more maths, more technology, more vocational training. *Useful* things — why do the kids of today never learn anything useful?...

Technology is advancing so fast that the latest gadgetry is obsolete the day after you get it out of its box. A desk-top microcomputer is now more versatile and powerful than whole roomsful of older computing hardware needing extra power cables to feed them. If you spend three months deciding whether to buy the Model A micro at £×00 you may find that the demand for the Model A has been so great that there is a three month waiting period; but that in any case the Model B (a much enhanced version of Model A with much greater memory capability and far more interface potential!) is now on the market at £×00 + £y and so everybody is going straight for the Model B... I can not help wondering about Model C. "To wait or not to wait. That is the question...!"

If you have read the first nine chapters of this book before reaching this chapter you will probably know more about information technology and its capabilities than I do at the time of writing chapter 10; because I am an educationist, and my work and leisure has brought me into contact only with a minute proportion of the potential applications. However, that partial acquaintance has been enough to set my mind racing to keep up with the possibilities and the predicaments.

How is society to cope with the effects of this technological revolution? Where will it all end? Are we to witness the end of 'a fair day's work for a fair day's pay' as we know it? Certainly we are seeing the end of much of the unskilled and semi-skilled work. The wood is not hewn nor the water drawn by hand any more. What will the adult lives of our averagely and below-averagely 'intelligent' youngsters be like? What are we educating them *for*? For work? For leisure? Or for the stress brought on either by overwork or underwork?

I can not be very specific about the answers to those questions in terms of a picture of what life may be like for the person in the street (and how much longer will it be before *that* expression becomes obsolete?!) later in the lifetimes of children about to start school. I can, however, be specific about the qualities those children will need to possess: because they will be the qualities that successful, satisfied human beings have always needed. However much technology may change the ways in which things are done, the human beings which the technology serves will not change. The pace of evolution is infinitely, thankfully, slower. People will still need compassion and understanding. They will still need to work cooperatively towards agreed ends. They will still need reliability and a sense of responsibility. More than ever before they will need the ability to adapt to new situations. They will need initiative to find directions in which to channel their energies and ambitions. They will need the strength to live with love and hate and fear and greed and grief, just as human beings have always done. "Plus ça change, plus c'est la même chose..."

So the question becomes: "How are today's children best enabled to learn these things; and how best may the new technology serve the eternal purposes of education?"

My experiences — as a child and as an adult, as a pupil and as a teacher — have led me to have a particular view of how people learn and how schools should be organised. That view will inevitably colour any description I may make of the ways in which IT could/should be used in schools and the benefits it could bring; but any bias I may have should not detract from the relevance of what I have to say for any school or any college or any university, anywhere; however Local Authorities and teachers (and very occasionally pupils) choose to organise them.

All children *want* to learn; and to that end they are capable:

of acquiring basic skills
of gaining intellectual power
of becoming socially competent
of developing through their emotional experience

In order to learn successfully they need three things:

(1) a belief in themselves
(2) a desire to succeed
(3) a habit of hard work;

and these three things are interdependent: you cannot have a measure of one without having a measure of the other two; and they act on one another to produce an infinite variety of positive/negative responses to stimuli. The question then becomes: how can IT help children to acquire such skills and powers and competences? How can it help them develop self-belief, ambition and the work ethic?

The environment children find themselves in can either actively encourage, or take a neutral stance on, or actively discourage this belief and this desire and this habit. One might say, for example, that children learn best:

when expectations for their intellectual, emotional, social, moral and creative development are of the highest order from the earliest age;
when they are given confidence in their own ability;
when they play an active part in their own learning;
when they work cooperatively rather than in competition with each other;
when parents are actively involved in the school, and in their children's education;
when their own culture and experience is valued.

So how can the new technology help to create and to satisfy such a set of conditions?

Just as all children want to learn, all teachers want to teach; but if optimum conditions are to be created for the effective organisation of learning for *pupils* we should not lose sight of the fact that the *teacher's* working conditions are of paramount importance. What about the quality of life for teachers? Unless you get the best out of *them* you will never get the best out of pupils, however hard you try.

Not surprisingly, the conditions we may choose to record as most likely to bring success are ones which probably apply to all human beings, with very little adjustment. Teachers work best:

when their working conditions allow them to make full use of their skills, experience and knowledge;
when they work cooperatively with each other and with their pupils;
when they are active in formulating the objectives of the school, and responsible for planning the curriculum.

In what ways can the new technology bring such conditions closer to reality for the teaching profession?

What conclusions may we now begin to draw about what kind of places *schools* need to be if they are optimally to serve the purposes of education for all the children who go to them? However much educationists may disagree about this or that detail of organisation or strategy, what has to be clear is that a school is a complex, subtle, living thing. It is a world in miniature; and within this microcosm children must be helped to learn how to develop all the skills they will need:

(a) to survive in the world as they find it;
(b) to take on from us the burdens of trying to change it for the better.

To these ends, different educationists may between them assert that our best schools should be seeking:

to serve *all* children in a neighbourhood;
to be coeducational communities;
to be democratically run;
to promote the initiative of pupils and teachers;
to avoid fixing ability labels;
to encourage internally created courses, externally moderated;
to encourage every teacher to teach, whatever other responsibilities s/he may additionally carry;

to involve parents and the community in the everyday life of the
school;
to have forms of government and extracurricular activities which
involve parents, teachers, pupils and councillors;
to make available a range of choices for children, while ensuring a
common core of basic study;
to meet not only the intellectual but also the emotional, social, moral
and creative needs of children;
to set themselves standards by which they are prepared to be judged.

When talking about Information Technology and new horizons, we are
therefore quite clearly not merely talking about more efficient ways of
passing on the same information plus some early 'hands-on' experience
and a computer-studies option for the brightest pupils in middle and
upper school. We are talking about ways in which the new technology
may make available to us the means by which we may translate sets of
aims and objectives such as the ones described above into effective
reality for all our pupils: for those who will fly highest academically,
commercially, industrially, professionally; for those who will run; and
for those who will walk.

It should, however, be the fervent wish of all of us that in these future
generations of adults who will inherit the earth from us, none need crawl;
and if that wish is to be fulfilled, then education must do much more than
make IT available as an essential tool for future generations of
professionals. It must harness the energy of IT to the need all schools
have to *'Educate' all* of their pupils to their full potential.

How much energy will that take? How could such information be
used? *Do* we yet have the technology to make the country's first bionic
school? Better than it was before: better ... stronger ... faster ...?!

The key word is 'resources'. It might help if we considered the
following argument in stages:

*Stage 1.   The key principle of comprehensive education is equality of
value*

Not equality of opportunity: opportunities being very often defined for us as those things we just missed.* Children can never be given equality of opportunity because by the time they get to school they are so unequally matched that to present them with an equal opportunity is to ensure that those to whom life has already given most (before they ever got *near* a school) will continue to profit most; and school will play its part in widening the gap between the swiftest and the slowest to unbridgeable proportions. Children can, however, be *valued* equally, and schools should seek actively to persuade each child that s/he is of great and equal value to any other, with huge potential for success: if only s/he will believe in her/himself enough, be ambitious enough, work hard enough ...

Stage 2. It follows that the school should avoid placing ability labels on children

Labels create expectations to which teachers and pupils alike will conform. Setting and streaming, many will argue, are devices which place unequal value on children: the most determined teaching and the most valued resources will often be devoted to top sets/streams, upon which the school pins its hopes of academic success and a good reputation; while the middle and bottom sets/streams pay the price in mediocrity or downright failure in the school's and society's terms. Not the best of starts for the majority of our children; not all that different, many would argue, from the old 11+ and the segregation of 'grammar' from 'secondary' children.

Stage 3. Learning should therefore be organised in all-ability situations

This is often referred to as 'mixed-ability teaching' — a misleading term, because any class bigger than one is a mixed-ability class. Mixed-ability, or all-ability, teaching is very commonly found now at least in the first year of comprehensive schools.

You may not go all the way with this line of argument; but I think

---

* May I recommend a very short book which says a very great deal about how learning should be organised? — Pat Daunt, *Comprehensive Values*, (Heinemann, 1975).

everyone would agree that even in a streamed or setted class there is bound to be a wide spread of ability. Teaching to an assumed norm, in the traditional way, will almost certainly either lose some at the 'slow' end or fail to stretch some at the 'fast' end; and there remains the problem of the lump in the middle. I think everyone would also agree that however much better it is in principle, it is far harder in practice to organise learning in the *all*-ability situation, where the mixture can often seem to be chalk and cheese. How *can* you cater for the needs of every individual in the group?

Yet, however one organises the learning group, is that not what must be done? How else are children to be given confidence in their *own* ability? How else are they to play a genuinely active part in their *own* learning? How else can our expectations be of the highest order achievable for *each* child?

The answer has to be resource-based learning. We must plan our schools and the resources within them in order that learning can be organised at a wide variety of levels in any location, using a wide variety of information sources which are freely and easily available to all teachers and all pupils. And this is where, to date, most schools come unstuck. There is no way that any individual teacher can do all that: stretching the brightest, encouraging the slowest, getting a shoulder behind those coasting along in the middle; finding the books, writing the worksheets, ordering the films, planning the trips, making the tapes; seeking to ensure that the curriculum is multi-cultural and positively anti-racist; striving to eradicate or nullify the sexism still seeping through most printed and media material while struggling to ensure that the curriculum is positively anti-sexist ... the list is endless.

All schools have tried to make progress along this road nevertheless; some more than most. Many schools now have 'resource-centres', which are not just libraries in the old sense, but repositories of resources of many different kinds — newspaper articles, tapes, slides, pictures, loops. Many schools have organised learning into 'areas': all the Maths teaching taking place in adjacent — and if you are lucky interconnecting — spaces; all the Sciences, the Social Sciences, the Languages, the English, the Design and Technology, and so on. Some few schools have organised their space into 'sub-school' areas: where groups of children may spend a large part of their school week in inter-disciplinary studies.

In well-organised schools each of these 'learning areas' will have its own resources well organised. Many schools in falling-roll* situations have used the much-needed space to reorganise for resource-based learning: setting aside rooms as 'satellite resource areas' which are subject- or sub-school based; for reprographic workshops, viewing rooms, careers information centres ....

Yet the problems remain. Just how much course-planning can we make time for? How much record-keeping and assessment? How much formulation of cross-curricular school policies? How much making and devising and encouraging and individualising...? There have never been enough hours in the school day.

The new information technology *can and should* bring the achievement of these most worthy aims, the fulfilment of these vaulting ambitions, to within our grasp. Data, once collected by anyone anywhere, could be made available to any pupil or teacher at the push of a button. What information does the school have on subject x? In what locations is that information stored? What is additionally available in the Authority's resource and information centres? Which museums, galleries, collections contain relevant material? What worksheets at which language levels are stored in which departments in which schools? The possibilities of data storage and retrieval alone are endless.

Video-discs are due to appear in Britain this year (1982). These discs can hold encoded material of any kind, and whole encyclopaedias can be stored on one disc the size of an LP record. Not only can the page of an encyclopaedia be displayed at will, but photographs can be brought to life: space shuttles soar into the sky above America, herds of wildebeest move across the plains of Africa .... The imaginations of children may be caught more completely and immediately than ever they were when having to pore over the indices of voluminous encyclopaedias. Ways are currently being found of linking a number of microcomputer or word-processor work-stations to a massive memory system. Eventually it should be possible to tie in microcomputers to a global library, making all world knowledge instantly accessible at any time in any place. Satellites will soon be launched capable of transmitting thousands of television programmes on hundreds of

---

* In many Education Authorities the number of children of school age is falling rapidly.

television channels anywhere in the world. If a programme has ever been made anywhere on any subject it should eventually be available at the touch of a button, with subtitles in the language of your choice ....

In the very best Education Authorities in the past, a resources-support team of up to twelve extra teachers may have been drafted into a school to spend three months cataloguing resources in that one building and producing a set of file cards for each department. With IT properly networked across an Authority — and the joy is that it *need not* cost an astronomical amount — the data filed by that resources-support team could be available to every school in the Authority. Schools could compare resources, share information; whole galaxies of teachers can profit from the energy of a bright sun anywhere in the educational universe. The whole S.M.I.L.E. network (secondary maths individualised learning experiment) could be contained in a programme which would suggest particular matrices to serve particu-lar needs of individual pupils, with additional suggestions of related materials and their location. And what is true of Maths is true of every other subject — without exception. Information storage and retrieval is a massive and obvious benefit, with a potential saving of millions of hours of teacher-time.

However, that is only a proportion of the total gain.

The pocket calculator is perhaps the first electronic computational device to be freely and cheaply available to entire populations of schoolchildren and teachers. Consider what educational possibilities calculators bring within reach of children. Calculators crunch numbers; and as an educational tool rank with audio and video tape recorders in the enormity of their value to education. Many many children (and adults) have never learned to think mathematically because they can not crunch numbers. They got lost on the way somewhere between chanting "three twelves are thirty-six, four twelves are forty-eight, five twelves are..." and "the square on the hypotenuse is equal to the sum of the squares on..." In mathematics, how can you learn to solve problems, test hypotheses, explore possibilities, check for accuracy/error (all of which activities are the stuff of learning in any field) if you can not crunch numbers? With a pocket calculator a child can do all of these things. It can carry out genuine research which will lead to genuine discoveries. Once a child feels that thrill of discovery the results will be stored in its memory banks far more reliably than any amount of mindlessly-repetitive basics-bashing can do. 'The path to knowledge is unfolded truth'; or as a child might say, 'finders keepers.'

I watched a child recently in a maths lesson. She had been assessed on entry to secondary school as 'borderline E.S.N.' (educationally sub-normal). Reading, 'riting and 'rithmetic were for her almost unscalable obstacles to learning. She was playing noughts and crosses on the computer with another child. In order to get your nought or your cross where you wanted it you had to do a little sum which flashed up in the square on the screen. "2–4?" it asked. "2–4, 4 is bigger than 2 you can't do it" was the confident and immediate response. Down came the stubby little finger on "O"; "WRONG" the computer burped. "WHY, sir?", was the indignant question. "Aha," replied the maths teacher, "let's find out." From teacher to computer to teacher to calculator to computer and back to teacher...; the 'variably-efficient-but-essentially-passive-recipient-of-information' model has been replaced by the far more exciting, far more stimulating, and therefore far more effective 'active-participation-of-the-learner' model. And the teacher as the organiser of learning is no longer alone.

For 'the concept of negative number' in this context read *any* concept. What are the ideas we want children to explore in the name of any subject? What activities do we want them to undertake? What experiences do we want them to undergo? They can work through programes at their own pace, with the computer deciding on the most appropriate path to move along, according to the nature of the responses the child is making to the questions the computer is asking. The game format is one which appeals very much to children, and the greater motivation which results can lengthen considerably the concentration span of the average or below-average child. Also the computer is patient: it will never get cross (providing no teacher has been silly enough to *program* it to get cross!). Children with learning difficulties may often therefore be happier with the machine than with an irascible or impatient human being; and less afraid of revealing mistakes. The immediate response and personal attention pupils get from the computer is also very satisfying and encouraging.

It all comes down to learning *how to learn* and how to take the kind of responsibility for your own learning which will guide you through all the learning you will go on doing throughout your life; until the day you almost learn whether dying is exactly like what you thought it would be — the final hypothesis.

What the new technology does is free people. It frees children from the slavery of data-acquisition which so often they were unable to relate to meaningful programming. It frees them to test and try and discover the essential *modes of thinking*: how to be logical, how to sift evidence, how to make choices, how to estimate, how to validate, how to predict consequences ... . It frees teachers to organise learning effectively in all ability situations, to team-teach, to coordinate resources, to assess and evaluate, to keep accurate records, to encourage group-work, to individualise learning ... . It frees Education Authorities to use their ancillary support services to a degree of efficiency unimaginable before.

So what has to start happening now, if these benefits are to be passed on to and through schools in the next two decades? Several things, all of them straightforward and obvious.

Teachers have got to get to grips with the technology. The only effective way to learn what computers can do for you is to get your hands on one and 'interface' with it: learn its language and it will do your bidding. You do not have to wait for an Education Authority to provide you with the hardware and the courses. £400 will already buy you a powerful microcomputer which will interface with your own television as a VDU and your own cassette tape recorder as a data store. £5.50 will buy you an excellent, widely available book which will enable you to follow a simple self-instructional course on the language of microcomputers and good programming techniques. £30 to the National Extension College will buy you access to a correspondence tutor with experience of your make of micro to take you through the course and mark all your assignments. It is all amazingly easy and cheap, particularly when you consider the power it will place at your disposal as a teacher.

Education Authorities must give top priority to installing computer network systems in schools. Systems are coming on to the market all the time. A communications network enables a number of computers to share expensive resources such as a printer and a disc 'file-server'. Very many stations may share the facilities of a single network. Any station can view any other similar station's screen, and messages may be passed between any of the machines.

The first stage would be to extend the network to the main departmental or sub-school areas within a school: perhaps ten to fifteen stations. As teachers learn more about their use, more software will be developed which will be of school-specific and/or universal relevance application. This will be available in the school's own data stores, and through links with the Authority's mainframe computer, and from other information retrieval sources such as Prestel and Teletext. Schools can then expand the network gradually. By the year 2000 I would expect there to be access to a computer for any teacher or pupil through a keyboard station in every classroom.

Textual intercourse with a computer is permissible at any age. Pupils should develop keyboarding skills and be given hands-on experience from as early an age as possible. Ideally, every child should have access to a calculator, a typewriter and a personal computer in their own homes. Teachers in schools and National Governments through the mass media should mount campaigns to bring this about. Schools must plan courses which ensure that children are given every chance to learn how to use a typwriter, how to use a calculator, how to use a computer; and I mean the word 'use' to be understood in its most positive and creative sense. Children must learn how to use these tools in the effective organisation of their own learning, as naturally and as easily as they use their teachers, and the other resources at their disposal.

My mind goes back to Chaucer's Clerk of Oxenford, "that unto logyk hadde longe ygo". Chaucer said of him:

"For hym was levere have at his beddes heed
Twenty bookes, clad in blak or reed,
of Aristotle and his philosophie,
Than robes riche, or fithele, or gay sautrie."
(*Canterbury Tales; General Prologue:* 293–6)

Those twenty books would have been manuscripts, painstakingly copied by monks: objects of comparative rarity and of great value; the collection of half a lifetime. What a revelation printing must have been: small wonder that renaissances of learning and reformations of beliefs were fired by this most powerful of fuels — the widespread availability of information. The labour of scholars in more recent times seems particularly poignant now. Mary Cowden-Clarke writes in her preface to the new and revised edition of her *Complete Concordance to Shakespeare* in 1881:

> "It is now more than half a century ago, when, on the 15th July, 1829, sitting at the breakfast table of some friends in pleasant Somersetshire, regret was expressed that there existed no Concordance to Shakespeare; whose works formed the Bible of the Intellectual World. Eager in everything, I resolved there and then that *I* would write this desired Concordance; and that very forenoon, while joining my friends in their walk through the fields, I took a volume of the Poet and a pencil with me, and jotted down the first lines of my book under B:
>   'Boatswain, have care.' *Temp.* i.I., etc.
> Sixteen years of hard work, but delightful work, sufficed to complete the manuscript."

Boatswain have care. Computers can now process hundreds of thousands of bits of information in a second, and output the results simultaneously on opposite sides of the globe in less than another second. There can be no doubt that the tide of the new technology will bring upon its flood changes as profound as any that are witnessed in our remembered histories. They will be changes which will affect schools as completely as they will affect all other ways in which we organise our living and learning; and we must all prepare for these eventualities, as thoroughly and as rapidly as possible.

Part Four

11

A Practical Guide

DAVID FAIRBAIRN

Director, The National Computing Centre Ltd

FOR MANY organisations, the introduction of information technology starts with the purchase of a small computer or a word processor. It is this step which so frequently causes concern and can lead to problems which are severely disrupting to the organisation.

There are essentially two problems facing the potential user of a computer if the organisation has no previous experience of the technology:

1. fear and prejudice which can make a purchaser vulnerable to sales pressure,
2. inability to recognise the implications of automating a previously manual system.

These apply whatever the application area — industrial control, business administration, educational systems are just some examples. The actual application area may determine which organisations are sought to provide help, or which books are read to provide information, but there should be a commonality of approach to selection and implementation of a system.

In preparing a guide to this, I am deliberately deferring a 'ten point plan' to later in the chapter since it is important to recognise that there is a growth process in which the two problems listed above must be overcome. It is therefore important to start with an open mind which says that automation may be appropriate — but possibly it may not be!

Does it help to read about it?

At the end of this chapter are lists of books and magazines which could be useful. Many of these are entertaining — particularly the magazines — but the question is whether they have real value in developing an understanding of how computers might be used. A methodical approach would be to use publications —

to gain understanding of computers and computing,
to find out how other organisations select and use computers,
to gain information about products and services,
to obtain ideas about selection and implementation.

The first of these — to gain an understanding of computers and computing — is unlikely to be achieved from reading journals. While it is true that many computing magazines have run series on 'So you're new to Computing', 'How does the Computer Work?' or some similar title, this is rarely in the context of applications. And it is in this context that an understanding must be gained by the intending purchaser. In fact introductory articles may confirm the fears and prejudices if they concentrate on computing technology and programming, facing the reader with the jargon of bits, bytes, PROMS and VLSI.

Although computing journals may not be helpful in this, there have been useful articles in many of the professional and trades journals and it would be worth checking through back issues of those appropriate to your organisation.

Books may be better in aiding understanding and good examples of general texts are *The Computer Book*, which supports the BBC series *The Computer Programme*, and Bradbeers book *The Personal Computer Book*. Others, such as *Make a Success of Computing in Your Business*, contain less detail but introduce concepts as appropriate in considering the requirements for computing.

So what are the fundamental ideas which must be understood? First and foremost there must be an appreciation of just what may be considered for computer solution — the capabilities and limitations of computers. With this comes a need to understand how information may be communicated to the computer and how information is held —in terms of working and backing storage. Beyond this, understanding is overtaken by information which, for example, can relate to the alternative media to provide storage, the quality and speed of a printer and, possibly, alternative means of data entry. Mistakenly, there is often felt to be a need to understand programming and intending purchasers of systems bewilder themselves trying to learn BASIC and become confused with reading about the relative merits of COBOL, FORTRAN or APL. It is sufficient to recognise that a computer application requires there to be a program — but writing this is not the job of the user.

Clearly, to some extent, this is an oversimplification and some application areas do require a greater degree of understanding. In particular if a computer is to be linked directly to other equipment, to perform a control or monitoring function, it will be necessary to understand aspects of interfacing. For most readers though who are interested in business, educational or scientific applications, the actual concepts which need to be understood are limited.

The second use of reading publications was to see how other organisations use computers. Here the various magazines do help and month by month, journals such as *Micro Decision*, describe the experiences of particular users. Study these case histories, for when they are well written they not only provide pointers to the viability of using computers, but also indicate some of the pitfalls of hasty selection or unprepared organisation.

Information on products and services features in most of the monthly magazines as well as the computing trade press, such as *Computer Weekly* and *Computing*. In general this latter category is only of interest to organisations which have built up experience and expertise. Probably the most important information is that relating to commercially available programs. For many users there already exist suitable programs for their applications, and information about availability, with in-depth reviews, is a feature of many magazines. *Which Computer?* is just one such magazine which contains news items about new programs, reviews of particular programs and surveys of programs for a particular purpose or application.

In addition to programs, the magazines provide information about the features of particular computers — important when you are considering possible future expansion and require to start with a system which offers this capability.

The final reason for reading publications — to obtain ideas about selection and implementation — is often the most neglected. There has, however, developed over the years a wealth of expertise relating to the purchase and use of computers, and much of this is as relevant to today's small systems as it is to the larger mini- and mainframe computers of data processing departments. For the purchaser of a computer, books such as *Buying a Business Computer* by Michael Turner, contain a distillation of this experience and others, such as the previously mentioned *Making a Success of Micro-Computing in Your Business* include this as well as aspects of the technology. Included in this category is the small audio package — *How to Choose Your Small Business Computer* — from NCC. This package offers the opportunity to listen perhaps while driving a car and then later to build on this with the information and check lists of the accompanying booklet.

After the computer has been installed there will be a continuing need to maintain and manage the system. Aspects of security, scheduling, program and data maintenance, documentation and archiving loom larger as use of the system increases. For this reason, I have included at the end of the chapter details of several books on computer management and data processing practice.

Is there a need for training?

The simple answer is 'yes', for an element of training focuses the attention on the ideas discussed above. For many this takes the form of reading — possibly making use of material such as that described above. For 'awareness training' though, increasing use is made of video materials or television series.

These forms of self tuition have their place but for many intending users of computers there is considerable benefit to be gained from the interchange of ideas of a public course.

Colleges, universities, private consultancies, computer retailers, professional training organisations and a host of other bodies offer courses with titles such as 'Introducing Microcomputing for Business' or 'Applying Small Computers'. Such a course, lasting perhaps two or three days or extending across several evenings, can provide a great deal of understanding, give guidance on the way to proceed and at the same time, stimulate an exchange of ideas which lets those attending relate their own ideas and problems to those of others. The problem is how to find a good and suitable course.

Possibly the most useful courses of this kind are those directed towards a particular user sector. If such courses have the blessing of a trade or professional association they can usually be relied upon to provide quality and, of course, a direct relevance. For general courses, though, look for ones which have built up a good reputation and, failing this, ask for a sight of the course documentation before registering. Well presented documentation lets you see the degree of care and thought which has gone into the course as well as giving an indication of the relevance of course content.

There is considerable variation in the cost of a course but it is false economy to try to find the cheapest. Training, like advice, comes very cheap when seen in the context of the total investment of cash and manpower in introducing computing to an organisation.

Just as there is a host of introductory courses there are also many which introduce programming and these are often promoted as being suitable for the newcomer to computing. Usually built around the programming language BASIC, it is certainly true that they are 'suitable' in terms of prerequired knowledge. However, their relevance is marginal and, indeed, may be counter productive if they encourage the user to develop serious application programs. Programming is great fun and many users like to find out about it but the serious application requires programs to be reliable, maintainable, flexible and well documented and this may only be achieved by experience which the user does not have and time which the user cannot afford.

Other courses which may be of interest relate to the particular applications being considered. A number of organisations have, for example, offered introductory courses on file handling, financial modelling or word processing. These generally introduce the concepts of the particular application and should make comparisons between a selection of the commercially available programs. They will, however, use a particular program as the vehicle for introducing concepts so, for example, a course might use FMS for file handling, VISICALC for financial modelling or WORDSTAR for word processing.

Once a system has been installed there is a continuing need for training which could, for example, relate to systems management, further applications or concepts necessary to consider enhancement of the system. In this last category, courses about operating systems or multi-user systems could be appropriate.

What are the Sources of Advice?

Apart from reading about computing or attending formal courses, there is a variety of sources of information, advice and consultancy. Many of these sources relate to business or industry in general and details of these may be found in publications such as the Department of Industry's *Technical Services for Industry* or *Sources of Information for New and Small Business* from Thames Enterprise Agency.

For those with a particular interest in the technology, one possible source of advice and information may be the local computer club. In London there is an Association of Computer Clubs and springing up around the country are local initiatives usually affiliated to the Amateur Computer Club or to Computer Town U.K. Details of these are given periodically in the journal *Personal Computer World*.

For many organisations, though, there is need for more formal advice and consultancy. In the area of industrial applications, information may be obtained from the DoI's Warren Spring Laboratory which administers the MAPCON scheme. This scheme maintains a register of approved consultants and also has available grants to enable feasibility studies.

In the business applications area there is no parallel scheme, but one interesting Government initiative is the establishing of Micro Centres in various parts of the Country. The first of these — Microsystems Centre — was set up in London by the National Computing Centre with help from the DoI. Microsystems Centre operates around an open house workshop which is equipped with about 18 small computer systems supported by a range of business software. Use of the workshop is free to any who are considering the introduction or growth of computing in their organisation. Although the systems are on loan to Microsystems Centre from manufacturers and suppliers, there is no commercial link with the trade and information and advice aims to be impartial. In addition to the free service, Microsystems Centre offers a variety of training activities and consultancy for the business user. For those wanting advice and guidance, the consultancy sessions may be as short as one hour duration.

Microsystems Centre has been operating successfully since April 1981 and it now forms a model for a Federation of Micro Centres which offer a similar range of services with the same objective of impartiality. These Centres, are being set up during 1982 with assistance from the DoI and details of the nearest Centre may be obtained from Microsystems Centre.

Consultancy in general may be obtained at a variety of levels and it is important to determine the level required. At its lowest level, consultancy is in the form of advice on suitability of applications and strategy for selection. This level requiring perhaps just a few hours of consultancy is not normally available from small consultants who are interested in longer assignments of possibly a few days duration. Where a longer consultancy is required it will usually involve help in selecting a shortlist of suppliers and giving assistance in the final choice and implementation. Beyond this, consultancy may extend to the provision of a complete 'turnkey' system in which the computer, programs, installation and training are all provided. In this last category in particular, care must be taken in selecting the consultant since the provider of 'turnkey' systems will have a trade agreement with one or more suppliers.

Consultancy is not cheap but, when compared with the costs of disruption to an organisation if computing systems are wrongly selected and installed, this may well be a price worth paying.

Starting in Computing — a 10-Point Plan

So far in this chapter, I have considered how you can get help and how you can attempt to become prepared for using a computer in your organisation. There comes a stage, though, in which with or without a consultant it is necessary to define a strategy which leads up to installing a computing system.

In considering a strategy I have assumed that the intention is to obtain a system for serious application — rather than for familiarisation and exploration. The total system is therefore geared to providing a service upon which the organisation depends and hence must not be subject to the vagaries of home grown programs. Software then will be professionally written — in most cases being commercially available packages, already tried and tested by other users.

It has already been suggested in the comments on training that the writing of programs by the user is counterproductive in terms of systems reliability and user time. What is often not appreciated is that, for a professional programmer, a reasonable estimate for writing and documenting reliable programs is about four lines of code per hour. A typical business program may run to several thousand lines of code!

The following 10-Point Plan concentrates on the selection process but it must be recognised that in parallel with this must be a plan of transition to the computing system. I will list the points and then discuss them in turn.

    i. *Needs* must be defined
    ii. *Alternatives* to computer application should be examined
    iii. *Quantities* should be defined
    iv. *Software* should be explored — special, general, tailored
    v. *Hardware* alternatives are considered
    vi. *Software/Hardware* evaluated
    vii. *Expansion* capability is considered
    viii. *Suppliers* are compared
    ix. *Support* is considered
    x. *Installation* is scheduled.

In considering these it is important to recognise that these represent a continuous process with a fair degree of overlap.

Needs must be defined is a process which should be made thoroughly before there is any commitment to use a computer. These may be general such as 'we need a more efficient system of stock control' or more specific such as 'output from the accounting system must satisfy the requirements for VAT returns'. Particular needs are as manifold as the variety of organisations but the following are a few questions which may be helpful after general areas of application have been considered:

? what happens if the results of a process (e.g. payroll) are an hour (a day, a week) late;
? what is the effect of the process coming to a halt (e.g. a power failure);
? who can have access to what information and when;
? for how long must information be kept;
? what would be the effect of losing the information;
? what outside agencies require access to the information;
? how are people employed in the existing manual version of the application.

Attempts to answer questions such as these may reveal some critical criteria which have been taken for granted. An existing manual invoicing system will have built up its own security, reliability and timing. In business analysis terms the system may have many flaws but, established by tradition and capable of human intervention, it is working. Computerisation of such a system, aiming to improve efficiency, will require much more precise definition and control.

For the first time user of a small computing system, it is likely that general needs (applications) will be in three categories:

applications for immediate implementation
applications for future implementation
applications which may be useful but are not essential (a bonus!)

At the stage of deciding whether to obtain a computer, it is the first of these which should be the sole factor. The others, though possibly important in choosing which system, will confuse, if it is the viability of a computer which is in question.

Although not a factor in the decision to use a computer it is interesting to note how frequently the third of these (useful but not essential) becomes a major area, at least in terms of time. An example could be a system purchased for business accounting which, when not required for the major application, becomes a word processor or is used as a planning tool. Word processing, in fact, as implemented on a general purpose computer has advanced considerably and in terms of flexibility and quality approaches that of the dedicated word processor.

Alternatives to computer application is the second step to be made before there is any commitment to obtaining a computer. It is at this stage particularly important to consider costs and people in the light of the needs already defined. It is very easy, having read a few advertisements, to gain the impression that £5000 worth of computing hardware and software provides a complete business accounting system (or a computer based training system, or a stock control and ordering system). What is forgotten is that the implementation of the system also incurs considerable costs. Costs in terms of manpower might be:

COST of data entry
COST of data updating
COST of data validation
COST of maintaining back up copies of vital information
COST of linking to other (manual) systems.

There is also the cost of disgruntled or demotivated employees and it is important, even in the case of the smallest computing system, to involve staff in the decision to use a computer and, if possible, in the selection process. This latter involvement is essential in the case of word processing or other applications involving extensive data entry. Typists and clerical staff should certainly be consulted on the use of a keyboard and screen.

So just what are the alternatives? The first, and possibly most effective, is a better tuned version of the existing manual system. The task of analysing, say, a stock control system with a view to using a computer will identify weaknesses and areas of improvement. Other alternatives may be the many card and chart based aids to accounting, scheduling and filing. At this stage, too, it is worth thinking about computing alternatives which do not involve obtaining a computing system. Computer bureaux, for example, offer services relating to most business applications either by batch processing in which data is sent to the bureau or by means of a terminal located in the user organisation. Bureaux appear expensive when compared with the cost of a small computer but it should be borne in mind that the service relieves the user of many of the burdens (costs) of managing a computer system (security, back up, maintenance, etc.).

Unfortunately this alternative is one which is too frequently rejected by departments of large organisations which do not recognise the services offered by a central data processing department. Budgets may allow departmental purchase and there may be apparent kudos in having a departmental computer but, when all costs are taken into account, it may be less cost effective than using the central machine. It must be admitted that a fair degree of blame must be attached to some computer departments. Working in an environment of big applications with long development times, many DP professionals were scornful of microcomputers and did not recognise either their significance or the changing scale of viable applications.

In many cases, even where an organisation does have a central computer, it is viable to purchase departmental systems. Here too, though, the computer department should be involved since there may be a small computer purchasing policy for the organisation (a limited range of compatible systems) and use should be made of the skills of that department.

Quantities should be defined is the final activity before embarking on a commitment to computing. It may be that having defined these, a possible computer solution is too expensive. Even if this is not the case, there is little point in approaching a consultant or seeking a quote from a vendor without the information to hand. For each application it is necessary to estimate:

file size
processing time constraints
access by users

It is then necessary to see whether the combination of proposed applications places any strains on a proposed system.

File size is clearly of vital importance in any business application. This will point to the type and size of backing storage required.

If the file structures are well defined in terms of the individual item which are to be held, it is a relatively straightforward task to determine size. The simplest way is to decide on the greatest number of characters required for each file item (30 characters for a name?, 10 characters for a stock code?) and accumulate these for the total number expected in the file. (Note: for numeric quantity items allow 7 characters per item, irrespective of the nature of the quantity.) To allow for the way information is stored on magnetic media and to give leeway for unanticipated expansion, this total number of characters should be increased by at least a half and preferably doubled. Storage, as you will be aware, is usually measured in 'bytes' and the number of characters estimated is equivalent to the number of bytes required.

Your reading of books and magazines will give you an idea of the capacities of various magnetic media — from about 100,000 bytes on the least densely packed 5¼ inch discettes to many millions of bytes on the sealed 'Winchester' hard discs. It should be pointed out, though, that use of the hard disc offers improvements in speed and reliability which may justify their use even when data volumes appear to point to floppy discs. It should also be pointed out that some form of removable medium (such as a floppy disc or digital tape) is required as back up to a hard disc. Very large files can create an inconvenience here if they have to be backed up to a much lower capacity medium and particular advice should be sought. Where this is the case, alternative suppliers should certainly be asked to quote configurations suitable for the estimated quantities and a comparison made of their proposed methods of backing up.

Processing time is, in general, more important in scientific and industrial computing than in business computing. In particular the so called 'real time' applications in which the computer generates a response (say control of a valve) following an input stimulus are clearly time critical. An element of 'real time' may also occur in aspects of educational and business computing in, for example, a computer based question and answer session or a retrieval system on stock availability. In these cases the time constraints are those which are tolerable to the human user — 4 seconds from human response to computer reaction? In general, delays are not caused by processing but by file retrieval —notable exceptions being a requirement for sorting and for the multiple permutations associated with scheduling. In these cases it will be necessary to try out the proposed hardware and software systems against actual or simulated data volumes.

Quantifying access by users relates to the rate at which data is to be transferred to and from the system. Questions which may be asked include:

? within a given time scale, how many people will require access to the computer — with what priority
? what are the time constraints on data entry
? what is a satisfactory speed of printing.

For the first of these, there is little point in selecting a computing system and *then* finding that there is conflict in, say, accessing a customer file and using the system as a word processor. If conflict does occur it may be necessary to consider some form of multi-access, networking or simply the acquisition of a second system. Advice in this is certainly required for in the case of a second system it is necessary to ensure that applications really are discrete and any thoughts on multi-access must take into account system performance, security and scheduling.

Data entry constraints may relate to the time scale in which large volumes of data have to be entered (such as preparation of reports on a word processor) or in which small amounts have to be entered in a very short space of time (such as a point-of-sale system). For large volumes it may again be necessary to consider replication of the system or some form of multi access while in the second it may be necessary to think of both the coding of information and the method of data entry. Taking retail as an example of the latter it would be intolerable to use, say, a 14 digit product code unless there was an alternative to keying, such as bar coding.

Print speed requirements will depend upon the volume to be output. Constraints are unlikely to determine the actual choice of computing system but they will have an effect on total cost if speed and quality are essential features of the printer.

So now you have done the preliminary work of assessing the viability of using a computer and have determined the constraints. You have probably some idea of the cost of a system although you are likely to have underestimated and it would be wise to allow at least 20 per cent more. Remember that the total cost of installing a computer is very much more than the capital cost of the equipment and that cost cutting in purchase may lead to higher costs of operating or disruption to the organisation.

You are now rea'dy to approach suppliers with your requirements to obtain (formally or informally) quotations for suitable systems. At its simplest your requirements can be specified in terms of:

nature of the organisation — or department
list of applications — immediate, future and 'bonus' as discussed above
particular constraints — e.g. relating to audit trails
data volumes, speeds, etc.

For more formal invitations to tender, it would be worth getting advice or you could refer to books such as *Buying a Business Computer.*

Software should be explored in terms of the application in general and the special needs which have been identified. The various alternatives can be:

general packages for a particular application (e.g. integrated accounting system)
general application package (e.g. file handler)
application area package (e.g. patient register for general practice)
commissioned software.

For many organisations, the first of these is an obvious choice — payroll, stock control, accounting and invoicing, production management are just some examples. Since these have been written without a particular type of user in mind it is important to determine whether the output satisfies internal and external requirements for your organisation. Facilities such as those offered by Microsystems Centre or other members of the Federation of Micro Centres are particularly useful since they enable comparison of packages to be made away from the pressures of a sales environment.

Word Processing, though strictly not in the same category can be approached in a similar way. Comparison of available packages will now concentrate on particular requirements — extended line, split page, flexibility of print controls — and the ability to link with other items of software such as file handlers.

File handlers are typical of the second approach to software in which the user tailors the package to particular needs. For departments in large organisations it is fairly common for computing needs to be satisfied by a combination of file handler, word processor and financial modeller. In selecting these it would be sensible to choose packages which can be linked so that, for example, the word processor can pick up information from a customer file and incorporate tabulations prepared using the financial modelling package. For many organisations the requirements of such packages are fairly simple but it is necessary to make sure that features (e.g. consolidation in a modelling package) are available and are not taken for granted. With both financial modelling and file handling packages it is necessary to determine capacity — to see whether they satisfy the volumes you have defined — and for file handling you should consider:

whether data entry or retrieval is the more complex (do you want entry to be via a form layout on the screen)
whether computation within a file record is required
whether statistics of the file are required (e.g. how many clients smoke and live in Yorkshire!)
complexity of logic in searching a file
whether several files share some common information (in which case so called 'data-base' packages should be investigated).

File handling packages may provide a framework for a variety of applications — stock files, customer files, etc. — and may avoid the necessity of acquiring a special application package. Similarly, financial modelling packages may provide a framework for simple accounting systems.

Packages for particular application areas are in some ways easier to investigate. The program now is written for a specific trade or profession and in many cases publications relating to that area have surveyed available packages. For some application areas, Centres in the Federation of Micro Centres carry a range of packages for a particular trade or profession and it is possible to use the workshops of these Centres to compare the alternatives. Microsystems Centre, which carries a range of software for medical general practice, can provide details of special software held at other Centres in the Federation.

If there is no commercial software available for a particular application, the remaining option is to commission the writing of programs. If this is done prior to selection of a system, the writing is normally part of the service provided by the consultant who is supplying a complete application system of hardware, software and support (a 'turnkey' system). Unless you are sure that no software exists, advice should be taken before commissioning program writing. Not only is this an expensive way of obtaining programs but also the resulting software is more likely to contain errors than software which is commercially available.

In exploring the availability of software you will also have encountered the vehicles for providing that software — operating systems and computing languages. The language may affect performance but otherwise is of interest to the programmer, rather than the user. Operating systems, however, are important in providing facilities for managing your system (copying discs, discovering the contents of discs, etc.) and determining the range of software available. Several operating systems, such as CP/M, BOS and Flex are not confined to single computer suppliers. This extends considerably the range of software of a single supplier. It should, however, be pointed out that at the cheaper end of the market, machines such as those from Apple, CBM and Tandy have a wide range of available software even though each has its own operating system.

Hardware alternatives are considered is thought by many intending purchasers to be the key question. In fact for many applications, a thorough exploration of available software should have narrowed the field considerably. Assuming that suitable software is available, choice will be further limited by considerations of expansion capabilities and the suppliers — which form two later stages of the 10-Point Plan. In addition though it may be appropriate to compare:

on the basis of aesthetics and ergonomics (involve those who will be using the system)
on the availability of graphics or colour.

Software/Hardware is evaluated is the stage at which you consider the actual running of the application on particular machines. Whatever you have read about the software, you now want to ensure that it performs at the speed required by your organisation and that it does not present difficulties to the user. Here again the opportunity to try out systems at a Micro Centre is useful but otherwise ask the supplier to suggest an existing user (a reference sale) or to simulate your application on a demonstration system. If the supplier will not provide these, beware and remember *it's a buyer's market!*

By this stage you should have spent some time looking at the various supporting manuals (the documentation) for the computing equipment and the programs. Remember that this is your source of information for installing the system, learning how to use it and referring to its capabilities. Poor documentation often reflects a poor product! Your other source of information for software is the instructions presented on the screen. Most programs today are 'menu driven', presenting at each stage a list of the various options open to the user.

Expansion capability is considered since you will require your system to grow. Right at the start of the 10-Point Plan was a definition of needs and one category suggested was that of future applications. Implementation of these may require enhancement of the system and capabilities include:

extending hard disc capacity
multi-access (several terminals to one computer)
networking (linking together of several systems)
intelligent terminal (linking the computer to remote systems).

With the growth of office automation and the provision of public information systems — such as Prestel — the desirability of enhancement may come sooner than anticipated at the time of initial purchase.

Suppliers are compared where the same system is available from several sources or there appears to be little choice between systems. Judging the quality of a supplier may require discussion with that 'reference sale' but remember that you are seeking a smooth transition to a computing system. To what extent does a supplier 'hand hold' through installation and if something appears to be wrong will your enquiry be fobbed off — 'you'll have to refer back to the manufacturer'? Computing equipment is complex, and frequently — unless installation is under the guidance of a consultant — instructions will be misunderstood or information appears incomplete.

Support is considered relative to the expected life of the computer. It will be necessary to decide on the level of maintenance required and whether this is provided by the supplier, the manufacturer or an independent contractor. In general this last category is preferred since the independent contractor should be geared up to provide a comprehensive service and the success of the contractor is wholly dependent on the quality of that service. Maintenance is not cheap and would normally cost between 12 and 15 per cent of the capital price per annum to provide a 24 hour turn round with repair or replacement.

Installation is scheduled is not really the final stage but is the constant reminder that installation does not start following placement of the order for a system. The transition from manual to computing system must be planned with users prepared (and possibly trained), provisioning (forms, instructions, furniture, etc.) made and a schedule prepared for tandem running of manual and computing systems until the latter can be relied upon.

In this chapter I have concentrated on the stages of selecting and installing a computer — principally for business use. When the computer has been installed it will be found that its effect is very different from that of other office equipment. Principally this is because there is a processing of information and this has to complement a host of other activities in the organisation (in terms of timing, availability, reliability, security, etc.). Over rather more than thirty years of commercial data processing there have grown up traditions and methods which facilitate this and many of these are relevant to small computers as well as to the larger machines of data processing departments. In particular the methods of systems analysis — prior to introducing new applications — and of operating standards should be investigated. The computer can be a great asset to an organisation but it will only be really effective if its use is in a well disciplined context.

Sources of help

1. MAGAZINES AND PAPERS

Which Computer?	monthly; includes 'Which Word Processor?'.
Practical Computing	monthly.
Personal Computer World	monthly.
Computing Today	monthly
Office Systems	monthly
Micro Decision	monthly.
Educational Computing	monthly; relates to schools computing.
Computer Weekly	professional trade paper.
Computing	weekly; professional trade paper.
Computer Management	monthly; controlled circulation. EEC Publications Ltd, Islington Green, London N1.
Infomatics	monthly; controlled circulation. VNU Business Publications, 53 Frith Street, London W1.

2. BOOKS

Buying a Business Computer, by M.J. Turner, Which Computer Handbook (3rd Edition 1980) — comprehensive aid to the management of selection and implementation.
Make a Success of Microcomputing in Your Business, by Pannell *et al.*, Enterprise Books (1981) — introduction to business computers and their selection.
How to Choose Your Small Business Computer, by J.M. Eaton, NCC (1981) — audio cassette and booklet available from NCC or Microsystems Centre.
Computerisation for the Small Business, by E.G. Cluff, Gower (1979) — good general introduction by an experienced computer practitioner.
The Computer Book, by Bradbeer, De Bono and Laurie, BBC (1982).
The Personal Computer Book, by R. Bradbeer, Gower Publishing, 2nd Edition (1981) — well written text introducing the technology and application of small computers. NOTE: This publisher has a range of books relating to Information Technology including *Choosing and Using a Word Processor, The Electronic Office — a Management Guide to the Office of the Future, Computers in Accounting and Auditing, Small Computers for Business and Industry*.
Installing a Small Business Computer, by P.A. Knight, NCC (1981). General guide to selection and installation.
Choosing Programs for Microcomputers, by J.E. Lane, NCC (1980). Includes useful guidelines to the selection of software.

In addition to the last two books, NCC publications offers several titles which are concerned with the management and operation of computing systems. In particular, the following help in establishing good procedures for effective use of a system:

Guidelines for Computer Managers;
Introducing Systems Analysis and Design;
Introducing Computer Programming, by W.G. Collin;
Using Computers — A Manager's Guide, by M. Peltu.

3. INFORMATION, ADVICE AND CONSULTANCY

Microsystems Centre, 11 New Fetter Lane, London EC4 — division of the National Computing Centre (NCC) concerned with use of small computers. Offers workshop, consultancy and training.

Federation of Micro Centres — DoI supported initiative with Centres having similar aims to Microsystems Centre which acts as the coordinating agency.

British Computer Society (BCS), 13 Mansfield St, London W1 — professional association, source of information particularly in relation to special interest groups (data-base, Information Systems, Handicapped, Schools, etc.).

Computing Services Association (CSA), Hanover House, 73 High Holborn, London WC1 — an association of bureaux, consultancies, software houses, etc.

MAPCON, Warren Spring Laboratory, PO Box 20, Gunnels Wood Road, Stevenage, Herts — for financing feasibility studies in industrial applications of microelectronics. List of registered consultants.

Council for Small Industries in Rural Areas (CoSIRA), 141 Castle St, Salisbury — information, some technical advice and details of further sources of help. Various local offices.

Association of Professional Computer Consultants, 109 Baker St, London W1.

Association of Independent Computer Specialists, Leicester House, 8 Leicester St, London WC2.

These are just some sources of help. Among general lists which may provide other sources are:

Technical Services for Industry, Department of Industry.

Sources of Information for New and Small Business, Small Business Unit, Thames Polytechnic — this useful guide is a forerunner to a more comprehensive directory and has been prepared in collaboration with the BBC and produced by Shell U.K. to accompany the BBC television series 'Business Club'.